DAY
ONE
YEAR ONE

Michael Hirshon © 2014

DAY ONE

YEAR ONE

BEST NEW STORIES & POEMS 2014

EDITED BY **CARMEN JOHNSON**

Published by Little A, New York

www.apub.com

Amazon, the Amazon logo, and Little A are trademarks of Amazon.com, Inc., or its affiliates.

ISBN-13: 9781477820964
ISBN-10: 1477820965

Printed in the United States of America

Cover illustration by Michael Hirshon
Interior design by Ashley Saleeba

CONTENTS

UNDER THE INFLUENCE

Michael Hirshon © 2014

A NOTE FROM THE EDITOR

A bizarre event kicks off a winning streak for a woefully bad baseball team.

A young entomologist attempts to explain love and heartbreak through a lab report.

A factory worker gets dosed with eyedrops that blur his vision before his shift every day.

Turnip-shaped extraterrestrials meet to plan their takeover of Earth, but struggle to stick to an agenda.

What's going on here?

Mind-bending scenes like these have been part of my reality for the last year while filling the digital pages of *Day One*. We wanted to publish a literary journal devoted exclusively to emerging writers, poets, and illustrators, and the book you're now reading constitutes a greatest-hits package, featuring some of our favorite work from the journal's first fifty-two issues. We've published messy breakup stories, workplace horror shows, postapocalyptic tales, and coming-to-America dramas. And every story is paired with rich, thoughtful, and sometimes comical poetry that explores the great topics: love, abandonment, and, of course, antiaging.

"It feels a little silly sometimes," Heather Monley, author of *Cat Man* (Issue 4), once said to me. "After all, what can I offer a world that already includes, you know, Chekhov? It's sort of like bringing cheap wine to what turns out to be a fancy dinner party: embarrassing, but at least you brought something."

Our contributors are indeed bringing something—something unusual, entertaining, and entirely their own. I remember the first time I read *Cat Man*, about a woman who enters a relationship with a man who is in the process of turning himself into a cat. I thought, *How beautifully strange!* The premise was fantastic, but Heather depicted a relationship as believable as any I'd read about. It's a story I'll never forget.

Short stories are about instant impact. A writer has only so long to leave an impression. With such a constraint, it's no wonder that the short story is often where writers take the biggest risks, choosing voices or scenarios that might not be sustainable for the length of a novel. I love stories that zero in on the tiniest, strangest, most fascinating moments of human lives yet also explode outward to reveal a character's life over a dozen pages. B.D. Mauk, whose story *I'm Your Shade* (Issue 25) takes place during a single night in an office, does something like this, creating a micro/macro view that's funny and sad all at once. B.D. and Heather and the other writers whose stories are gathered here take us to destinations as real as our workplaces, as strange as our desires.

"What excites me about poetry is also, I think, what is most difficult," writes Mary-Kim Arnold, whose charming "Minor Saints" appeared in Issue 8. "I am trying to play with language, the sound of words, the rhythms of syntax, the way words and letters look on the page, while also trying to evoke some kind of emotional response in the reader . . . to present something that is both recognizable and startling for a reader. Not to alienate, but to make contact."

Michael Hirshon, one of the talented illustrators for *Day One*, found inspiration in Mary-Kim's poem for *Day One, Year One*'s cover: "I dreamed you / at my sink in your socks."

"I look for the most emotionally charged scenes," says Michael. "I pay attention to the small details that reveal something big, and then do my best to capture it in an illustration. There's something about standing at a sink in socks that tells us all we need to know."

I've had such fun watching our stories and poems transform into vivid cover art, especially the gorgeous mechanical heart Forsyth Harmon conjured for our debut issue in October 2013, which featured Rebecca Adams Wright's *Sheila*. Forsyth's drawings are like lavish hieroglyphics; she has an uncanny ability to pluck an image from the text and turn it into a stunning symbol as mysterious and elegant as the words it represents.

One year in to *Day One*, the stories and poems and drawings follow me around like invisible thought bubbles. When I'm dressing for cold weather, wrapping a scarf around my neck, I imagine Maryanna Hoggatt's illustration for Valerie Geary's *This Great Love*. I pass by a fruit vendor and I'm back reading *Highway with Green Apples* (the first story published in English by the extraordinary South Korean writer Bae Suah). I overhear someone talk about the quirks of her new boyfriend and I think, *Have you checked for a tail?* And whenever I'm stuck in a particularly long meeting, I imagine turnip heads and I smile. Read enough good stories and they will live with you.

Happy reading!
Carmen Johnson

Michael Hirshon © 2014

DAY
ONE
YEAR ONE

Maryanna Hoggatt © 2014

THIS GREAT LOVE

VALERIE GEARY

I

Cuthbert Wilson tries to wiggle his toes—and can't. He tries to bend his knees—and fails. He's lying down. Where? Some dark room, in a bed not his own. Dim light through a curtained window reveals shadow-shapes crouching nearby. A chair heaped and draped with dark coats hunkers in the far corner. Near his head and off to the right, a computer beeps repetitively, glowing a faint red and reflecting off the screen of a television bolted to the opposite wall. The bed has rails. The blankets covering him are bleached white. The walls, the ceiling, and what he can see of the floor: white on more white. A hospital room then, because his legs have stopped working—though how this all happened remains unclear, his memories over the past few hours either missing completely or too muddled and broken-down to be of any use.

The last thing Cuthbert Wilson does remember is this: walking his usual workday route, from his house on Southwest Jefferson, twelve blocks to the Standard Insurance building on Fifth, at his usual brisk clip, shoulders straight and arms swinging in a lazy rhythm. Right, left, right, left, up, down, up, down, excuse me, pardon me, coming through. The orthopedic insert in his right shoe had shifted and rubbed wrong against his heel, but other than that his legs were working just fine. And before that? As far as he remembers,

3

this morning started out like all previous mornings. Nothing out of the ordinary, nothing that might have brought him here.

His alarm rang at 5:00 a.m. exactly. He took a seven-minute shower, shaved, and dressed in a white-collared shirt, navy-blue tie, pressed brown slacks, and matching brown suit jacket. He combed his hair, parting it straight down the middle the way he always does. At 5:20 a.m., he was in the kitchen making the same breakfast he always makes: scrambled eggs and toast for one. He turned the small television on the counter to QVC and drank his usual cup of instant coffee with his eyes closed, imagining his house filled with laughing, talking people who didn't care that he never talked back. With the last sip, he choked down a multivitamin and a low-dose aspirin, and then washed and dried his dishes, and returned them to the cupboard. He spent exactly two minutes brushing his teeth, one minute flossing, and thirty seconds rinsing with mouthwash. Then he went to the living room and slid the lid off his fish tank.

"How's the water this morning, old girl?" Goldie swam to the surface, her orange lips puckering and sucking up her food flakes. Cuthbert watched her swim circles until his wristwatch beeped. He could watch Goldie all day, and sometimes on lazy weekends he did, but today was a Thursday, a workday, and he had a time card to punch. He grabbed his briefcase, and the sack lunch he'd packed the night before, and left his house. He remembers making it to Salmon and Park. And after that? The very next thing he remembers is waking up here.

Using his arms, he tries to push himself into a sitting position. A lightning bolt of hellfire and needles shoots up his spine. He cries out and falls back against the pillows. The dark coats in the corner spring to life, rushing and fluttering toward him like angel's wings or demon smoke.

Through the darkness, a voice: "My love! You're awake! Oh, thank you, Lord!"

This is no devil then, no eater of souls, no Grim Reaper, and no Saint Peter opening heaven's gates, ushering him into the light. Here beside him: a woman. Plain and simple. She brushes her hand across his forehead, bends, and kisses him above his left eyebrow. The smell of her is familiar—rain and mothballs and a hint of vanilla. Familiar, though he can't think why that would be.

She takes his hand. "Are you in terrible pain, my love? Shall I call the nurse?"

He tries to answer, managing only a weak and pitiful croaking sound.

She hushes him and tucks the blanket tight around his shoulders. "You gave us a real scare today."

Who are you? Where am I? What's happened? He makes that sad croaking sound again, and the woman squeezes his hand.

"Let's get you a sip of water." She reaches for a cup and, for a moment, her face is visible, backlit by the window.

Cuthbert has one of those minds that never forgets a face, and hers is one he recognizes. Maybe he's seen her around the office. Maybe he even hired her. He sifts through his memory, recalling the face of every woman currently employed at Standard Insurance, starting at the top of the alphabet—Cynthia Adams, Benny Alton, Jessica Blackwood, and on and on, all the way to Gloria Zuckas—but none of them are her. He digs deeper, sorting through the faces of every woman who's ever worked at or interviewed for Standard Insurance during his twenty years in human resources, but finds no match. He knows he knows this woman; he just doesn't know from where.

She lowers a paper cup to his chin and tucks a straw between his lips. "Here we are. Careful, slow sips. That's it. Now, see? Isn't this nice?"

Cold rushes into his mouth, down his throat—soothing, fresh, and it *is* nice, so very nice, to be cared for this way. He can't remember the last time someone looked after him like this, showed him such concern. She dabs drool from his lips and chin with a soft cloth and asks if the pillows are comfortable, if she can get him anything else. His own mother never even cared this much. She lets him take another sip of water and then sets the cup on a nearby table.

She says, "Close your eyes, my love. You're safe here with me. Close your eyes and sleep."

He doesn't feel especially drowsy, but his eyes close anyway, his whole body relaxing. A few more hours can't hurt. After all, he hasn't been sleeping well these past few weeks. Someone's been calling his house at all hours of the night and hanging up. Wrong number probably, and what a nuisance. Yes, he may as well sleep a while longer since he has the chance.

"I'll be here when you wake up." The woman says this so quietly, Cuthbert wonders if maybe he's dreaming and that's why she seems familiar, because she's his own creation, a fantasy pieced together from glimpses, scraps of memory, and yearning. This makes sense, and so he falls into a deeper sleep, rather pleased with himself for having figured the whole thing out. His alarm will ring at 5:00 a.m. sharp, and he will wake, and it will be a day like any other day, and he will walk, as he's always walked, his usual route, twelve blocks from his house to the Standard Insurance building on legs that work just fine.

———

Somewhere in Cuthbert Wilson's subconscious mind, a memory rises to the surface and with it, terrible panic. He jerks from sleep, arms flailing, grabbing at shadows. He thrashes and groans, desperate to get away, but his legs—they aren't working. And the woman—she is still here beside him, trying to hold him down, telling him everything's going to be all right, though clearly it's not. A door opens, and hot white light floods the room, blinding him momentarily. He blinks and blinks until the world re-forms.

A man with blurred features and coffee breath bends over him and says, "Mr. Wilson, you're at Legacy Emanuel. I'm Dr. Richmond. I need you to take a deep breath and try to calm down. There you go, that's it."

Cuthbert stops thrashing, but he is not calm. The doctor steps away to check the machine monitoring his vitals, and the woman comes into view again, standing close to the window, her back to the glass, one arm cinched around her ample waist. She rocks a little on the balls of her feet and gnaws her lower lip. He stares at her and, beneath this cold, fluorescent glare, yes, now he sees clearly. Now he is certain.

She is the same woman from this morning, with the pale moonface and too-small nose, the raised mole on her ill-defined chin, the dull-brown unkempt hair, unraveling to her shoulders. The very same woman who materialized from shadows near the apartment building on the corner of Salmon and Park, who pleaded, "My cat! My poor, poor baby! It's stuck in the dryer vent. Please, help me!"

Now, of course, knowing what he knows, with hindsight what it is, he realizes how stupid he was, falling for it. But this morning, she was just a woman who loved her cat, and he, a man who understood exactly how an animal could become a person's whole life. He followed her into the apartment building and down a dark hallway that seemed to go on forever, but instead of opening the door marked "Laundry," she pulled him toward another door at the end, a red door, without a single word of explanation. He should have known when he saw the stairs that something was wrong, but he was thinking of Goldie and how terrible it would be if he lost her the way this woman had lost her cat, and so he continued to follow. Up four flights of stairs to the roof.

The roof! Oh God—what a fool he was!

"Mr. Wilson?"

How long has Dr. Richmond been calling his name?

"Mr. Wilson, can you tell me what day it is?"

He can't stop staring at the woman.

Dr. Richmond, noticing her for the first time, says, "Ma'am?"

The woman shrinks a little, hunching her shoulders.

Dr. Richmond asks, "Are you family?"

When she doesn't answer, he turns to Cuthbert again and says, "Mr. Wilson? Do you recognize this woman?"

Yes, but she does not belong here.

"Mr. Wilson? Do you want her to stay?"

No. No, he does not want her to stay.

Dr. Richmond is waiting for his answer. Cuthbert gathers his strength and shakes his head. Vigorously.

"My love?" the woman says, her voice trembling, barely a whisper.

"Are you certain, Mr. Wilson?"

He nods, and pain shoots up and over the top of his head. He falls against the pillow, exhausted.

The woman lets out a sharp gasp, a strangled whimper. "Oh, Cuthbert. My darling."

"I'm sorry, ma'am, but I'm going to have to ask you to leave." Dr. Richmond gestures to the door.

"I'm his wife." The woman clenches her fists and sets her jaw and lifts her head. "I'm staying."

"I understand this is a difficult time for both of you, Mrs. Wilson," Dr. Richmond says. "In cases like this, with the extent of memory loss not yet known, it's hard on everyone. But our top priority now is to keep your husband calm and relaxed so his body can heal. And if having you wait outside makes him more comfortable, then we have to respect that."

The woman says, "Cuthbert?" But he refuses to meet her gaze.

Dr. Richmond says, "Please, Mrs. Wilson. Don't make me call security."

The woman's cheeks turn red, and tears gather on her lashes. She says his name over and over and pleads with him to let her stay, and there is a single brief moment where Cuthbert worries he might be wrong about her, maybe it's like Dr. Richmond says, maybe there's something he's forgetting, but before the idea can take hold completely, Dr. Richmond leads the woman by her elbow to the door.

"Please," she says. "He needs me here. Let me stay. Who else will take care of him?"

"Your husband's in good hands, Mrs. Wilson. I promise you. We're taking excellent care of him." He moves her gently into the hallway. "The waiting room is around the corner to your left. I'll be out to speak with you shortly. Please."

She goes, and Cuthbert is safe now.

Dr. Richmond returns to Cuthbert's bedside and waves a penlight in his eyes. "Mr. Wilson, do you know who the current president of the United States is?"

He swallows, and then nods and croaks, "Obama."

"Very good, Mr. Wilson. Very good." Dr. Richmond puts the penlight back in his pocket. "And your address? Do you remember that? Can you tell me where you live?"

"1192 Southwest Jefferson Street. Portland. Oregon." Every word is a physical struggle, though he has no trouble remembering.

The doctor turns to type something on the computer, and Cuthbert Wilson slides his left hand under the sheets. With his thumb, he rubs at a gold band circling his ring finger, wondering how it got there, for he's quite certain he wasn't wearing any rings at all when he left the house this morning.

II

Love found Prudence on the very same Tuesday that Mrs. Barbado in A12 suffered a heart attack.

At the ungodly hour of 5:55 a.m., sirens ripped through the neighborhood, wrenching Prudence from dreamless sleep. Red and white lights flashed across her ceiling. She got out of bed, put on gray and tattered slippers to match her gray and tattered bathrobe, shuffled to her bedroom window, and pulled aside the curtains just a sliver—enough to see, but not enough to be seen.

Parked crooked against the curb like a broken tooth, an ambulance blocked the northbound lane. Though no one but Prudence seemed to care. Her fingers twitched the curtains. She pushed her shoulders straight and gathered a trembling breath. She'd count to six and then march out her front door, straight to the driver, and give him a piece of her mind. Certainly there was no need for such rude behavior. Certainly they could park straight and close to the curb so that cars coming and going could pass without trouble. Certainly they didn't need to use such loud sirens and bright lights this early in the morning. Before she could start counting, three EMTs came into view.

Prudence recognized Mrs. Barbado by her round shape and dark skin, and wasn't at all surprised that she was the one they were taking away. People were always tramping in and out of A12 at all hours, day and night, and what a ruckus: thumping music and clinking glassware, loud conversations and explosive laughter. "Life is a fiesta, *mija*," Mrs. Barbado had told her once when they passed in the hall and Prudence reminded her of the building's quiet hours. "You must embrace it while you can. You must live full and loud."

But Prudence knew that nothing good ever came from such debauchery and decadence, and here was her proof. The paramedics lifted Mrs. Barbado into the back of the ambulance, slammed the doors shut, and drove away.

Prudence started to pull the curtains closed again, but the first bright streaks of dawn gave her pause. Pink and purple and shimmering orange, bleeding over rooftops and spilling through the gray streets and into her window. She hadn't seen a sunrise since she was a little girl. She pushed the curtains open wider. A ray of burnished gold splashed through the glass and frolicked across her forearm, setting her pale-blonde hairs aflame. *And how wondrous,* she thought. *How incredibly marvelous.* She twisted her arm and made the sun dance.

The clock radio on her nightstand read 6:45 a.m. exactly.

———

Since that morning, Prudence has become convinced that there is most definitely a God and no such thing as coincidence. Everything happens for a reason—we only need to be paying close attention to recognize the direction the Universe wishes us to take. When Prudence thinks back over the course of her life, she has no other choice but to believe in destiny, because had certain events played out in a completely different order, she might have gone on living her entire life without consequence, lonely and alone.

If her parents hadn't died one right after the other, then the bank would never have taken the house, and Prudence wouldn't have been forced to move into the Park Tower Apartments. And if she hadn't moved into the Park Tower Apartments, then she wouldn't be living next door to Mrs. Barbado, whose late-night revelries had most certainly brought about her untimely collapse, which in turn, brought the ambulance. And if not for the ambulance, Prudence's natural circadian rhythm would have gone uninterrupted and she would have slept soundly until exactly 9:00 a.m., as she had every day before this one. And if she had slept until 9:00 a.m., she would have never opened the curtains, never watched the sun rise, and never seen the man with his hair parted perfectly down the middle walk past her window at the exact moment she was marveling at the light and shadows playing across her arm. And though he tried to make it seem a small thing and unimportant—a quick turn of the head and then face forward again, a glance and nothing more—Prudence noticed. And she felt it too. A flicker, a jolt. A terrifying but not altogether unpleasant feeling of falling from a great height, and unlike anything she had ever felt before. She watched him from her window until he disappeared around a corner.

She did not know where he had come from or where he was going or whether she would ever see him again. She knew only this: they were supposed to be together. She belonged with him, and he with her. Theirs would be the kind of love she had dreamed of as a little girl and stopped believing in after Simon Sommers stole her innocence in the back of his father's station wagon, laughing when she cried and leaving her in a Wendy's parking lot to find her own ride home. The kind of love you could wait and search and pray for your entire life and still never find. And yet somehow her Great Love had appeared, by destiny or miracle or the perfect alignment of planets, and it mattered very little that she did not know his name, and he did not know hers. They had from now until forever to work out the details.

———

At 5:55 a.m. the next day, Prudence woke naturally, without any alarm, her circadian rhythm adjusting to love. She showered, dressed, ate breakfast, and was waiting at the window, the curtains pulled halfway open, by 6:30 a.m.

At 6:45 a.m. exactly, he appeared. Prudence had two minutes—from her apartment to the corner of Broadway—to study him through the glass.

His suit was a slightly darker shade of brown today, but he carried the same black briefcase in his right hand, wore the same navy-blue tie in a Windsor knot, and parted his hair the same—straight down the middle. His jacket was too big in the shoulders, but his slacks were pressed and creased, and his shoes polished to gleaming. He walked slightly hunched, and if someone veered too close, he shuffle-hopped to one side to avoid brushing against them. He never waved or tipped his head or spoke to the people he passed. Eyes forward, he marched and marched, bobbing his head in perfect rhythm with his stride. He walked with the quick step of a man who has someplace important to be. A man with purpose.

This morning his steps did not falter and his eyes did not dart. He turned the corner and out of sight without a single gesture of love. Prudence pressed her hand to the cool glass and smiled. He was shy, something Prudence understood very well. She just needed to give him more time.

She gathered her knitting basket, moved the rocking chair from its usual place in front of the television into a ray of sunlight and settled down to watch the people moving to and from wherever, going on about their busy, happy lives. As she watched, her fingers flew—a flurry of yarn and needles, a coming together, a beginning.

Men in suits and women in heels talked on cell phones. A mother pushed a baby stroller. A pack of teenagers wearing backpacks and matching uniforms jostled by, shoving each other, laughing and talking so loudly their squeals came through the glass. A homeless man, carrying his entire life in a garbage sack over his shoulder, shuffled to the corner bus stop. Two older women in Lycra jumpsuits and colorful headbands speed-walked around the block, passing in front of Prudence's window several times. Three large dogs dragged a ponytailed blonde toward the park across the street.

Every day these people were here, whether or not Prudence opened her curtains to see them. So many hearts beating. So many lives weaving together and apart. So many words jettisoned into the silence. Yesterday the walls were too thin, the space between her and them too narrow, the balance she'd struck too fragile. Remarkable, how one glance changed everything. How suddenly bold love had made her.

She wanted to push open the front door, sing and spin and dance in the streets, tramp through rose gardens while little birds flitted alongside her, spreading her joy with their feathers. She wanted and wanted and wanted. The whole world expanding, stretching possibility.

Her fingers moved faster, transforming the blue-gray yarn into a scarf that would complement perfectly his navy-blue tie.

———

At noon the boy came with her groceries. He knocked three times. "Mrs. Alton? Mrs. Alton, you there?"

She had never bothered to correct him before—that she wasn't a Mrs., but rather a Ms. or Miss. Today she opened the door smiling and said, "Call me Pru."

The boy frowned and shoved the sack of groceries into her arms. "Fifteen seventy," he said. "Plus tip."

She gave him a twenty-dollar bill and told him to keep the change.

He stared at her as if she'd lost her mind, and maybe she had. She didn't even double-check the dead bolt after she closed the door; she didn't knock six times and six times more. She simply locked the door—once was good enough today—and then carried the groceries into the kitchen and made her usual lunch of grilled cheese and tomato soup. Maybe tomorrow she'd go to the store and buy her own groceries. Maybe.

Prudence knitted and watched and waited and wanted, and finally, at exactly 4:15 p.m., he came around the corner going the opposite direction. She held her breath as he passed in front of her window, and released it in a rush when he was out of sight again. Just like earlier that morning, he came and went without acknowledging what was growing between them. But Prudence wasn't worried. She would wait by the window as long as it took— days, weeks, years, if she had to—for him to make up his mind and choose love. Choose her.

Every day she followed the same routine: wake at 5:55 a.m., shower, dress, eat breakfast, then settle into her rocking chair by the window and knit. At 6:40 a.m. she would set aside the blue-gray scarf, now long enough to wrap several times around his neck, and stare out onto the street. At 6:43 a.m., he would appear. At 6:45 a.m., he walked past her window. At 6:47 a.m., he disappeared around the corner. In the afternoons he returned, walking past her window again, and Prudence watched and Prudence waited, and every night she suffered disappointment. They carried on in this fashion for some time, and then, and finally, exactly three weeks to the day after that first glance, he gave her another sign.

She almost missed it. 6:46 a.m. and he had already passed her window and was almost to the corner where he would turn and disappear when, without a single faltering step, he switched his briefcase from his right hand to his left.

Prudence clutched the nearly completed scarf to her chest and said, simply, "Oh."

He turned the corner and was gone.

"My love," Prudence whispered.

She finished his scarf with an hour to spare.

At 4:00 p.m. Prudence dragged a large cardboard box from her closet and began to dress. Long johns first. Then jeans and her mother's moth-eaten snowman sweater. Over this, she wore her father's black trench coat, which was missing a button. To complete the ensemble: three pairs of wool socks, red rain boots, an orange knit cap, her father's leather driving gloves, a red scarf, aviator sunglasses, and a dab of vanilla-scented oil behind each ear.

At the front door, she counted to six and then turned the dead bolt six times. She breathed in through her nose, out through her mouth, in through her nose, out through her mouth. She knocked six times, opened the door, and knocked six times more before finally stepping outside for the first time in nearly two years.

The asphalt heaved, and the sky dropped low, pressing her flat. She blinked and reached for something to hold on to and tried to think of what her old therapist would have said about this situation. "It's all in your head, Prudence, my dear. The world is only as dangerous as you believe it to be." Of course, Prudence had gone to only one session, deciding within the first five minutes that the therapist was crazier than the patient, and certainly not worth the $200 an hour she charged. Her father would have slapped her on the back and said, "Buck up, old sport." Her mother would have scowled and said, "Really, Prudence. There's no need for such a fuss. Come, dear, people are staring." Useless advice, and none of them loved her, not really, not the way *he* did.

Prudence tucked her hand in her pocket and knotted her fingers in his blue-gray scarf. The sky receded. The asphalt stilled. And here he came around the corner. He smelled like a used bookstore. She double-checked that her front door was locked, and double-checked again, and then hurried to catch up with him.

Two blocks west, he turned left onto Southwest Jefferson and walked another few blocks to a row of narrow townhouses. His was on the far end, a winter-storm gray, the trim and door painted red, a basket of purple fuchsias hanging from the porch eaves. He pulled a stack of envelopes and magazines from the mailbox, dug in his pocket for his keys, unlocked the door, and disappeared inside.

Prudence watched all this from the opposite side of the street. As his door swung closed, she darted into traffic. A car honked and slammed on its brakes. She pulled her orange knit cap low and shied away from the car, making it to his small front porch in time to hear him shout, "Goldie, I'm home!"

She had a moment of panic that he was not alone, that there might be another woman, and then, when there was no response from Goldie, relief and a flush of shame for doubting him. So maybe Goldie was a dog—though Prudence hoped not, as she was allergic—but there was no barking, no click-clacking of nails on linoleum. A cat? Prudence did so love cats. She listened at the door another few minutes, listened to his silence. How she longed to see inside, to watch him move about the rooms. A fly on the wall—certainly that was not too much to ask.

A woman passing on the sidewalk below paused and gave Prudence a hard and narrow stare. Prudence pulled away from the door and pretended to look for keys in her pocket. The woman left, and Prudence knew it was her time to go too. Her feet were starting to itch, her clothes to feel too hot. Before leaving, she traced the numbers and letters stickered to his mailbox: "1192, C Wilson." She traced them over and over until she had memorized the curves and swoops of each one.

Her love lived here. He slept and ate and showered and dreamed here. Her love, who finally had a name.

She took his blue-gray scarf from her pocket, touched it to her cheek, and then hung it over the doorknob. Hand pressed flat against his closed door, she whispered, "Sweet dreams, C Wilson, my love."

She smiled the whole way home.

———

The next morning he came around the corner wearing her scarf. True, he wore it wrong—had it wrapped around his neck two times instead of the proper six, so the ends dangled nearly to the ground—but he was wearing it, and that meant something. As if that wasn't love enough, when he passed her window, he smiled. Barely smiled. A twitch, really. A movement so small no one but Prudence would have noticed, because no one loved him as much as she did, but a smile nonetheless. She hadn't expected so much so soon.

She had precious few seconds before he turned the corner and disappeared. She tugged on the long johns and her mother's sweatshirt, her jeans and boots and her father's leather driving gloves. She dabbed vanilla behind her ears. On her way out the front door, she grabbed her red scarf and her aviator sunglasses. She didn't have time for her three pairs of socks, the orange knit cap, or her father's trench coat; and she didn't have time to knock six times and then six times more.

On the sidewalk, Prudence didn't hesitate. Fearing she had already lost him, she shoved past two mothers with oversized strollers and almost knocked an old woman to the ground. She turned the corner onto Broadway just in time. There he was, several steps ahead of her and almost out of sight. The blue-gray scarf fluttered and flapped, and people moved out of its way. She followed him to a skyscraper on Southwest Fifth Ave.

The building stretched taller than any she had ever seen before. Up and up and up, the top disappearing inside low-hanging clouds. Prudence reached to pull down her orange knit cap but then remembered, horrified, that she had left it at her apartment. Too late now. Her love marched up a dozen concrete steps and disappeared through a set of revolving glass doors.

Prudence unwrapped her scarf, pulled it over her head and around part of her face, and followed him into the building.

Inside, her love was lost in a crush of people wearing suits and carrying briefcases. A bank of elevators on the far wall swallowed men and women in whole groups and took them up and up through the center of the skyscraper where Prudence imagined the elevator doors opening again on the very top floor, and those same men and women stepping into a gray office made of clouds.

Prudence stood inside the revolving doors and tried to catch her breath. Strangers moved around her, splotches and blurs in her peripheral vision. When someone brushed against her, she flinched. When someone said, "Excuse me," or "Watch it," she had to clinch her fists tight around the edges of her scarf to keep from crying out. She tried to whisper his name, to imagine the letters in her head like a spool of yarn unfurling—*C Wilson, C Wilson, C Wilson*—but it didn't help. Inside this vast and sprawling marble-floored lobby, Prudence found nothing steady to which she could cling, and no safe corner to hide in.

A young man with a thin mustache and white gloves approached her. Prudence fixed her eyes on the gold buttons adorning the cuffs of his black suit jacket. They sparkled magnificently.

"Ma'am?"

The badge clipped to his lapel read "Security."

"Ma'am? Are you all right?"

She forced her eyes up and saw that he was smiling. Keeping tight hold of her scarf, she said, "It's so loud in here."

He stared at her the way people so often did. Like she was crazy or dangerous, or both. The lobby was clearing out. Soon it would just be Prudence and this man alone.

He asked, "Are you here to meet someone?"

"Yes." Prudence shook her head. "I mean, no."

His smile faltered.

"I mean, not exactly and sort of." She had never been very good at this kind of thing. She exhaled and tried again. "I have an appointment later this afternoon, but unfortunately I lost the paper where I wrote down all the pertinent information." She liked that word, *pertinent*—it was a college word.

"Do you remember who you were meeting?"

"Mr. Wilson."

"No first name?" He walked toward a tall mahogany desk in the center of the room.

She followed. "I believe it starts with a *C*?"

He tapped a keyboard, frowning at a screen. After a few seconds, he smiled at her again and said, "Lucky you. There's only one C Wilson in our directory."

"Oh?" She leaned against the desk.

He nodded. "Cuthbert. Does that ring a bell? Cuthbert Wilson."

For a moment all other sounds ceased, and there was only his name, echoing through the lobby and corridors of her mind: *Cuthbert Wilson, Cuthbert, Wilson.* It was the sound of brooks babbling and church bells ringing and babies laughing, of every beautiful song she had ever heard. Cuthbert Wilson: the name of love.

His name stayed on her lips the entire eight blocks back to her apartment. And all day—until 4:00 p.m., when she returned to her place by the window to wait for him—she stood in front of the bathroom mirror and practiced their names together. "Mr. and Mrs. Cuthbert Wilson. Mrs. Prudence Wilson. Cuthbert and Prudence Wilson. Prudence and Cuthbert. Cuthbert and Prudence," and then she couldn't help herself. She giggled and started to sing, "Cuthbert and Prudence sitting in a tree, K-I-S-S-I-N-G."

———

The phone rang only once before he answered.

"Hello?" His voice was raspy and deep and made Prudence swoon. "Hello?" he said again, louder, with more force. "Who is this? Who's calling?"

In her mind, Prudence said so many wonderful things about love and fate and the strange course of their lives, how they had found each other even after all this time. But when she opened her mouth to speak the words aloud, all she managed was a wistful sigh. Cuthbert Wilson hung up.

An hour later, Prudence dialed his number again. She'd found it easily enough in the phone book—there were only two *C Wilsons* listed, but the minute she'd heard his voice, she knew she'd found the right one. She had his number memorized now.

"Hello? Hello?" He waited several long and silent seconds, and then said, "I think you have the wrong number. Please stop calling."

If Cuthbert Wilson knew who was on the other end of the line, he wouldn't hang up so quickly—Prudence was sure of that.

———

In the morning, she was waiting in her usual spot by the window, when a brown sedan pulled up to the curb. The driver, a young man with a long, dark ponytail, went around to the passenger door and helped Mrs. Barbado out of the car and into the building. She had been away for so long, the apartment so quiet, Prudence had forgotten about her almost entirely. The door to A12 opened and closed, and a few seconds later the music started. Most of what Prudence could hear through the wall was a thumping bass, but every few beats she caught trumpeting horns or clashing cymbals. She was surprised at her foot tapping, her hips swaying gently. She was surprised to be smiling. Maybe in a few days she'd bring Mrs. Barbado a tater-tot casserole. Yes, that was a lovely idea. She started to make a grocery list in her head: mushroom soup, ground beef, tater tots, cheese—

Cuthbert Wilson marched into view. He passed the brown sedan and then Prudence's window. She rushed out the door, thinking today was the day. Today she would shout his name and he would turn and they would . . . She turned the corner too quickly, expecting her love to be several blocks ahead, and ran right into him. He stood frozen, head tipped up, staring at something in the sky.

She and he. Prudence and Cuthbert. Two asteroids careening alone through empty space for so many, many years, and now, and here, and finally: colliding.

She felt him against her—the structure and weight of his bones, the heat and strength of his blood. And he felt her, too. And he turned. Turned and looked her straight in the eyes. Steel-gray flints sparking with something like recognition.

"My apologies. I didn't mean to block the sidewalk, but it's just," and he lifted one finger, a single perfect piano-man finger, above his head. "Have you ever seen a cloud shaped like that?"

Prudence forced herself to look up. A puffy white cloud bobbed alone in the vast sky, stretching above them like so much blue silk. It could have been anything: a rabbit, a turtle, a heart, a polar bear French-kissing a toad. It could have been anything, but the cloud wasn't as important as the fact that he had stopped here, breaking his routine, and waited for her to come around the corner. It was something and nothing and everything—this shape that wasn't a shape, this simple, drifting cloud.

"Remarkable," Cuthbert Wilson said, staring at her, and she at him.

He left her standing there, barely breathing, as though what they had shared was no more monumental than two strangers crossing paths, lives intersecting briefly, before carrying on their separate ways. Prudence wondered at the burning sensation under her skin, the sudden rush of warmth to her cheeks and the back of her neck. *I must be dying,* she thought. *And love has killed me.* Someone brushed against her, shouting at her to move out of the goddamn way. Jolted, Prudence turned and ran the half block back to her apartment. She locked the door, drew the curtains, and spent the rest of the day in bed, beneath her blankets, trembling.

———

That evening Prudence dug through cardboard boxes and garbage bags piled in her closet until she found her mother's jewelry box. She opened the lid and sifted through long strings of pearls and silver bracelets, hoop earrings and ruby necklaces, until she found them: two nearly identical gold bands. One was wide and meant for a finger larger than hers. The other was delicate and thin, and slipped perfectly onto her left hand. She held the ring up to the light. It glittered and sparked. She took it off again, and then dropped both rings into a small black velvet bag. She tightened the drawstring, slipped the bag onto a long red ribbon, and tied the ribbon around her neck so that the rings rested close to her heart.

———

Her mother told her once that finding true love was like playing the lottery. Buy enough tickets and, with a little luck, you might someday strike it big. Prudence prefers to think of love as being struck by lightning. You have to be in the exact right place at the exact right time, and it only ever happens once.

Her time has come. Today is the day. The Universe has brought her to this moment, this very one, and she is ready.

Prudence opens her front door at exactly 6:30 a.m. and finds a place to stand in the shadows and wait. For him. For Cuthbert Wilson. Her one true love. Her lightning strike. Here he comes now around the corner, wearing the scarf she made for him. He walks the usual route, in the usual way, at a brisk clip, shoulders slightly hunched, and arms swinging in rhythm at his side. Right, left, right, left, up, down, up, down, and on and on . . . except for . . .

Except.

Today.

Except.

See? There. He's limping.

Prudence watches his right foot carefully and, yes, there and again and not just a fluke: a hitch up, a shuffle forward instead of a firm step, as if there is something in his shoe. A pebble or a thorn. They are side by side, and then he is passing her. Now. She must do it right now.

Prudence steps from the shadows, reaching for his sleeve. "Excuse me?"

He stops, turning toward her. She hesitates only a second, hoping he'll speak first and make this easy, but he doesn't and, when she says nothing else, he shakes off her hand and starts to walk away.

"Please," she calls after him. "Wait." And when he stops and turns again, she says the first thing that comes to mind: "My cat! My poor, poor baby! It's stuck in the dryer vent. Please, help me!"

She reaches and grabs his sleeve, tightens her grip around his wrist, and pulls him back to her. Through the heavy linen, she feels his forearm tense and flex, and something unfamiliar and wild snaps awake inside her. Her thoughts and all reason are falling, collapsing, and there is a surge of heat rising in her chest, and then her teeth are chattering, her skin is stretched too tight. There's no turning back. She has him now; she must never let go.

She says, "This way."

He follows her, asking for the name of her cat, where the poor thing is stuck again, and how in God's name did he get there? She doesn't answer any of his questions, only leads him into her apartment building and back and back through the narrow hallway without any real plan of what to do next.

She keeps tight hold of his arm, fearing that if she loses him, she will lose herself. If she lets go, she will break free from the earth and float loose, drift high into the atmosphere, too high, all the way to the sun where she will explode into a million broken, burning pieces.

He points at a door marked "Laundry" and says, "Through here?"

She pulls him farther on, and he begins to drag his feet a little.

"Wasn't that . . . ?" But he doesn't finish.

They are almost to the other side of the building, to the back door that opens out into a small and sad forsaken garden, but before they reach it, Prudence turns a hard right.

"Where are you taking me?" He twists his arm, but Prudence is stronger and leaves him no other choice: he follows her up four flights of stairs and through a red door that leads out to the roof.

The wind is bitter up here, sharp and cold, and it claws them apart.

Prudence situates herself between Cuthbert Wilson and the door, the only safe way off this roof.

Free from her grip, he takes a step backward and away from her. "What are we doing up here? Where's your cat?"

I will explain everything, she wants to say, but the wind rips her words from her mouth and her hat from head. Her hair flies in a frenzy, tugging her scalp. She spreads her arms as if to try and capture what she's lost, and finds herself blinking and blinking into the sun. When she looks back at Cuthbert Wilson, he is an angel, a god.

"Your cat?" he asks again, with a mixture of disbelief and fear.

Prudence holds out her hand, but he doesn't take it.

He shuffles closer to the ledge. "Listen. If there's no cat, then I really just . . . I need to be on my way. I'd hate to be late for work over this."

She appreciates his composure, how he smooths down his jacket lapels and readjusts his grip on the briefcase. How he rearranges the scarf around his neck, the scarf she made for him, so it falls in two perfect cascading blue-gray waterfalls over his stomach.

"It looks lovely on you," she says. "Really lovely. Matches the color of your eyes brilliantly, which is a rather unexpected, but pleasant, surprise. I picked the color to match your tie, actually. But what a happy accident—if I believed in accidents, which I don't. Do you believe in accidents, Cuthbert, my love?"

His hands are up around his throat, his fingers brushing, caressing the scarf. He freezes and then starts to unwind the scarf slowly.

"No," she says. "Please. Leave it."

Twice around. Three times. One end growing longer, unraveling to the ground.

"Please," is all she can manage to squeak as he finishes unwrapping the scarf.

He drops it in a lonely heap at his feet.

"I'm going." He takes a step forward, making a motion to go around her, but she matches his step, blocking his way.

"Cuthbert, please. Did I do something wrong?"

He shakes his head and takes a small step backward. His brow creases, and Prudence understands now his insecurities, how he is afraid to accept the love she is offering and needs her to show him the way. He switches his briefcase from his right hand to his left.

"It's okay to be scared," she says. "I was scared once too. But ours is a Great Love like the great loves of old. Romeo and Juliet. Tristan and Isolde. Bill and Hillary. We are better together. Powerful and strong. I don't work without you. And you—you don't work without me."

He's still shaking his head. "What are you talking about?"

"You don't have to be scared anymore." She bends and picks up the scarf, shakes out the bits of dirt and small rocks, holds it out to him again.

But he doesn't take it. He shakes his head harder now, like he's trying to wake himself from a bad dream.

"Cuthbert, listen to me—"

"How do you know my name?"

"Oh, my love. Your name is etched on my soul. And mine on yours."

She reaches for him; he backs away.

"Listen, ma'am, I'm sorry, but I think there's been some kind of terrible mistake." He keeps shuffling backward. "You said your cat was in trouble. I was only trying to help. That's all. I don't know who you are, and I don't know who you think I am—"

"Do you believe in fate, Cuthbert?"

He doesn't answer.

"Do you believe in God?"

The sky stretches above them, the color of burned sugar. Five pigeons wing past, skimming the roof's edge, dipping, weaving, flashing out of sight.

"*I do,*" Prudence says, close to him again, as close as yesterday on the street when he spoke to her for the very first time. "Before we were even born, this day was planned, laced into the fabric of existence. The Universe has conspired to bring us together, my love. We are each other's destiny."

She reaches, strokes his cheek with her fingers. He flinches away from her touch.

She does not mean for it to happen. If she'd had any say in the matter, she would have chosen a different ending, but the Universe, in all its infinite wisdom, chooses this: his foot catching on a pipe protruding from the roof and tipping him over backward, his fingers reaching, brushing hers, but he is too heavy and slips from her grasp. She tries but cannot keep him from falling.

No more than a minute after he lands on the sidewalk below, as many seconds as it takes her to run down the stairs, she is beside him, pressing her fingers for a pulse, leaning to feel his gasping breath on her cheek. He is alive, as she knew he would be—the Universe would not part them in this manner, not now, so quickly, violently, not after all they've been through.

She takes the rings from the pouch around her neck, holds his left hand in hers, and says, "As long as we both shall live."

Cuthbert Wilson's eyelids flutter open only briefly before closing again, but it is all the commitment Prudence needs. She pushes the smaller ring onto her own finger and then leans over and kisses his bloodied lips.

An ambulance is on its way—the sirens rejoicing, marking this day of love. With only seconds until they arrive, Prudence takes Cuthbert Wilson's keys from his pocket and slips them into her own.

III

Days have passed. Weeks. So many, Cuthbert Wilson has lost count. And still, his legs are useless. During this time, only the doctors, specialists, physical therapists, nurses, and administrators have come to see him. There is no one else. His parents are dead. He's an only child. When he called his boss, his boss said, "Tough break, old man," and gave him the phone number for a disability insurance company. None of his coworkers sent flowers or get-well cards, because they did not know he was here; or if they did, they did not care. A reporter tried to interview him a few days after it happened, but

Cuthbert turned him away. This isn't any kind of story he wants to share with the world.

He watches television with the volume low. QVC, sometimes. Soap operas and talk shows, too. The news. Reality TV. Whatever's on—for the company and the feeling that he's not alone, not entirely. The nurses open the drapes, letting in blinding white light. When the nurses leave, Cuthbert closes the drapes again, more comfortable in darkness. At night, he dreams of falling. He dreams, too, of the woman. And when he is awake, he stares at the shadows lurking in the corner and tries to guess her name. Something old-fashioned, he thinks, something hard to spell.

Sometimes, when the nurses have gone and the television is off and the drapes are closed, he cries for Goldie, because she can't possibly be alive, not after all this time, without anyone to feed her and clean the algae off her glass, to tell her about the sun and the rain and what ridiculous things humanity got up to today. Sometimes he wakes and his pillowcase is damp, and his heart is broken.

———

The day he's been dreading finally arrives.

Dr. Richmond smiles, claps Cuthbert on the shoulder, and says, "Well, my good chap. Time for you to go home."

They have done their best for him. Two surgeries and enough pain medication over time to put down an elephant. They have come in every day to work with him. He is able now to use the wheelchair and get around—mostly—on his own, to dress and shower and feed himself, so when they ask about his home support system, he lies and says, yes, he has someone. He has no one, and there is still so much more therapy to do and another surgery in a few months. A long road, they say, but he is stable now and the odds are in his favor to walk again someday. Most people cry joyful tears; they laugh and smile for this news. Cuthbert asks if he can stay a few weeks more—he's not sure he's ready, you see; he's still in so much pain.

Dr. Richmond shakes his head and claps him on the shoulder again. "Sorry, chap. We need the bed."

The nurse brings him a sack of clothes—a pair of brown slacks, pressed and folded perfectly along the seam, a long-sleeve white shirt on a hanger, a silver-and-blue-striped tie, a clean pair of socks and underwear, his everyday work shoes polished to gleaming. He recognizes his clothes at once, but he does not wonder very long about how they came into the nurse's possession. He is distracted, fumbling to dress and, at the same time, worried about how he's going to make it home. It is too far to walk—roll, he means—and he does not know which bus can take him close enough, if there is even a bus at all. He sighs, buttons the last button on his shirt, and then leans back against his pillow to rest.

A few days ago, for the first time since his fall, Cuthbert moved his big toe, which seems such an insignificant thing, but Dr. Richmond said it was wonderful. He also said that if Cuthbert had fallen a few inches more to the right or left, if the building had been even a half inch taller, they would not be discussing the probability of a full recovery or anything at all for that matter. If the world had spun a little faster on its axis that day, or a little slower, if a butterfly had flapped its wings, Cuthbert would probably be dead.

"Mr. Wilson? Your ride is here." The nurse pushes his wheelchair close to the bed. "Are you ready?"

He nods, grateful they've arranged something for him, so he doesn't have to sit on the curb, waiting for a bus that might never come, as strangers gawk and stare.

Down to the lobby, and when the elevator doors open, the nurse pushes him into a stream of people who pretend not to notice how broken he is, though he can feel their pity, hear their sighs of relief that it is him, not them, who suffers so. He does not see her right away, but when he does, he slams his hands onto the wheels, bringing them both—himself and the nurse—to a sudden stop.

"Mr. Wilson?" The nurse bends down, and a bit of her hair brushes against his cheek. "Mr. Wilson, is everything all right?"

She's standing outside the gift store, beside a giant toy giraffe. Her hair is combed and curled, and dyed a darker shade of brown. She is wearing a pale-green sundress, spotted with tiny white flowers. She smiles and lifts one hand to wave. In her other hand: the scarf. The one she made. For him. She takes a tentative step forward.

"Mr. Wilson?" The nurse tries to push, but he keeps his hands clamped over the wheels.

It would be easy enough to tell them there's been a terrible mistake. He can't go with this woman—this stranger. She's the freak who tried to kill him. But then, that's not exactly true, is it? After all, wasn't he the one who followed her up to the roof? He who lost his balance? She did not push or threaten him, only made grand professions of love and destiny. Only offered her heart.

So maybe he had overreacted.

Cuthbert releases the wheelchair, and the nurse pushes him the rest of the way. They stop in front of the woman, who crouches beside him and wraps the scarf six times around his neck.

She smiles and brushes her thumb across his cheek. Her hands are soft. She smells like rain and laundry detergent. She says, "Let's get you home."

The nurse is still here. He can change his mind, have her call a cab. Or the police.

Cuthbert curls the tassels of the scarf through his fingers and stares at the automatic glass doors sliding open and closed. An old man gives his arm to an even older woman, helping her to the front desk. A teenager pushes a middle-aged woman in a wheelchair. Another woman carries a toddler on her hip. For all he knows, these people are strangers. That man, that woman, that child. They might know as much about one another as he knows about the woman who knitted him this scarf, who bends close to his ear now and says, "You won't believe how much Goldie has grown. Oh, but she'll be so happy to see you!"

Cuthbert spins the gold band on his finger.

"All right, then, Mr. Wilson?" the nurse asks.

Cuthbert is surprised to find himself nodding.

The nurse steps back from the wheelchair. "He's all yours, Mrs. Wilson."

Who is Mrs. Wilson? he wonders. And then the woman from the roof grabs the wheelchair handles and pushes Cuthbert out the hospital doors, moving carefully over the slightly raised threshold. His car idles at the curb. The woman opens the passenger door, then says, "Here we go," lifts him under the arms, and swings him into the seat like he's no heavier than a child. He finds her strength comforting and holds her longer than he means to, lingering with his nose pressed into her hair. He breathes in deep and catches the faint and familiar scent of vanilla. The woman does not push him away.

When he lets go and settles back, she reaches across and buckles his seat belt, pulling it tight. "How's that?"

He nods. She stands there another moment longer, holding the door open, lingering. Then she leans over again and her lips brush briefly against his cheek.

Before he can say anything, it's over, and she is pulling away, saying, "It's so good to see you again, my love. I've missed you dreadfully. Me and Goldie both."

There is something in her voice, the way she says Goldie's name, something that makes Cuthbert feel a little less in pieces, a little less alone, and he wonders if this is what people mean when they talk about love.

She starts to close his door, but he stops her and says, "I'm sorry . . . They never told me your name."

About the Author

VALERIE GEARY is a full-time writer who lives in Portland, Oregon. Her short fiction has been published in *The Rumpus*, *Menda City Review*, *Boston Literary Magazine*, and *Foundling Review*. *Crooked River* is her first novel. Find her on Twitter @valeriegeary or at www.valeriegeary.com.

Valerie on Writing
This Great Love

Ian McEwan's *Enduring Love*. I read this book many years ago and am still haunted by it, by this idea that with a passing glance—a single, brief encounter—the entire course of someone's life can change. Coincidence becomes fate becomes destiny; a butterfly flaps its wings, and a story is born.

Anton Chekhov's "The Huntsman." At the end of this story, there's a striking paragraph in which a woman is watching her estranged husband disappear over a hill, and there's a desperate ache to the imagery, a reaching loneliness. Yet there's a boundless hope, too, that someday, impossibly, he might return to her. This dichotomy intrigued me enough to start brainstorming my own story, which eventually became *This Great Love*.

My sister. She knits me charming hats, cozy socks, gloves to keep my fingers warm. She knits and knits, crafting so many beautiful things from yarn and love. I think of her every time I wear something she's made. So when I was drawing Prudence in my mind, when I saw her struggling to connect, it seemed only natural that she would take up needles and knit something special for Cuthbert.

A broken back. Shortly after I started writing *This Great Love*, I slipped off the bow of our sailboat and landed hard on a metal cleat, breaking my L4 transverse process. A painful injury indeed, though nothing close to what poor Cuthbert endured! Five weeks' bed rest, and my bone healed completely on its own. But during those immobile days, when moving even my big toe caused pain, I was able to imagine and really get a sense for how much worse it would be without my husband around to take care of me—how impossible life would feel, and how lonely, too.

Social anxiety. I think, on some level, most everyone struggles with stepping out bravely and making meaningful human connections. I know I do. As a self-diagnosed shy introvert, I prefer books over concerts, and tables for two over crowded house parties. I have spent my fair share of lonely hours sitting in front of windows, watching the world pass by, and, yes, I absolutely tapped into those feelings and fears when writing *This Great Love*.

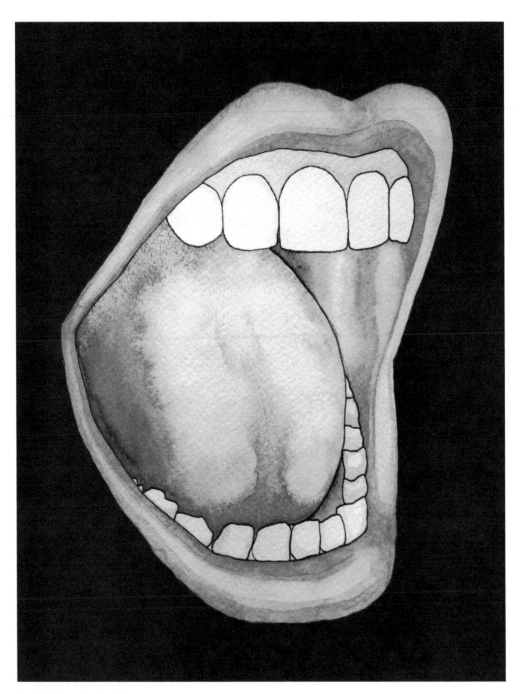

Forsyth Harmon © 2014

I'M YOUR SHADE

B.D. MAUK

There isn't much to say about the *Midweek* offices themselves, where for the past six years I've worn down the speckled blue carpeting of the assistant editor's windowless office and, more recently, the editor-in-chief's windowed one. Just now I am lying on the floor of the latter, or actually five inches above it, on an inflatable air mattress, waiting for Jon, my dead boss, to appear.

I think of the carpet as blue, which is what a man standing at full height under strong fluorescent lighting might call it at first glance. Although on closer inspection—say, by a man lying on an inflatable air mattress, the floor virtually in his face—it's possible to see even in near-total darkness that the carpet has a speckled or dappled texture, resulting from the many constituent fibers woven about the plastic grid-work, and that these individual fibers are of at least eight identifiable hues (beige, rust, navy, cerulean, and so on), which from the vantage of six feet create the believable appearance—the gestalt, you might say—of a single color: the grey-blue of the sea under a sky that won't rain. This somber color emerges from the component fibers, none of which is, on its own, the precise shade of their aggregate. I've had opportunity to study the carpet closely and at length since being rousted from home by Mandy two nights ago, and I've found that, in keeping with the rest of the *Midweek*'s decor, the carpet is a cheap thing: The "ear to the ground" editor will notice several threads uprooted by the sharp corners of chair legs and file cabinets, as well as slight molehills where the fabric doesn't lie flush with the floorboards. These hills pop out a centimeter or so from the ground and can be pushed in to change the floor topography elsewhere, the result of which is an added third dimension to the dappled pattern of the carpet: a depth of carpet. From my supine position on the mattress, I'm reaching out to push on one molehill now, imagining as I do so that this will activate a secret wall panel or trapdoor installed by Jon—who in my fantasy would have prepared this final test for me while still alive—revealing some covert communiqué from beyond the grave. But when I push on the hill, I hear no clicking latch or electronic chime, and the only visible change in the office is that a new hill pops out several inches away, purple and zit-like in the gloom.

What else in the office? Exposed wires; cheap plastic blinds; windows in which loose panes rattle against the elements. Flimsy interoffice walls of plywood, foam, and fabric. Once, I'd believed that the Spartan decor was another manifestation of Jon's stinginess. In fact, the paper is bankrupt. By cutting our freelance rates and strategically misplacing the interns' paychecks, I've managed to scrape together printing and distribution costs for the past few issues, but if nothing more is done, we'll soon be shuttered. In the months since assuming Jon's position, I've grimly learned to appreciate every little savings, such as the fact that our flimsy walls obviate the need to buy actual corkboards for any staff. (*The writing's on the wall,* he used to say when incensed, slapping a worker's papered wall until thumbtacks rained onto the offending employee's head.) By lifting my own head, I can see where on one such plywood wall I have tacked up the months' worth of working proofs, P&Ls, and press releases of my brief tenure. Beneath these, I've pinned more permanent fixtures: business cards, typefaces, a photograph of Mandy. Even in the dark, I can make out—dimly, of course—the layered surface of this wall, my working wall, on the other side of which is the now-vacant assistant editor's office. I know just what Jon would have said about my papered wall: *Fitz, a disorganized office is the sign of a disorganized mind.* The very sight of it would probably have sent him into one of his famous rages. But I like that when a gust of air circulates within my office—as happens when the door is opened quickly—a few of the pages lift and wave with ghostly comport, like strips attached to a vent. The papers worry in the air for a moment, seeming very much alive and purposeful—as they could not if each corner were pinned into permanent arrest.

At four thirty today, following just such an episode of waving, in the wake of Bernice's departure from my office, I turned from my computer to gaze out the north-facing window. The windows are an undeniable perk of my sudden, otherwise tragic, promotion. They look out on Main Street, where the small-town vista offers respite from the voices that Jon used to speak of: the murmur and yelp of ledes, layouts, half-column ads, local politicians and business owners, crime-scene witnesses, conspiracy theorists, the flea-market din of the classifieds—the whole rancid rabble that harangues the small-town editor, who must be the paper's ombudsman, design team, accountant, and head writer all in one. How pleasant to look up from one or another of these myriad jobs and see not pages of unfinished work, as was the case in my former office (where the desk grotesquely faced my working wall), but to see instead the placid Spielbergian town itself. There is something affirming in this. As Bernice's antiseptic perfume lingered in the air, I lifted my gaze to the framed view of the Larwood post office and corner store, and was briefly overwhelmed. My throat tightened, and I was thankful the office secretary was no longer present to witness the small mammalian noise I made. Though I am thought by my coworkers and wife to be a reserved and even stoic figure (especially compared to my predecessor, a man of seriously unstable moods), for a moment I felt near hysterics as I looked out into the bright afternoon. The bankruptcy had me feeling in over my head—*beleaguered*, as Jon would have said. (He was always beleaguered, would pull me into his office, enraged or depressed, clutching a cigarette despite office regulations, and with his head in his hands would intone my name: *Fitz Fitz Fitz. I've really stepped in it now.*) Now I am the one beleaguered, driven not to illicit indoor smoking but to staring out my window at Main Street in exhaustion. So much as glancing at anything inside my office forces me to consider not only the budget crisis that had been looming for a year and which Jon kept hidden from me, but also Jon's surprising and unpleasant death, which occurred just weeks after his announcement, and fast-tracked my promotion in what I suspect was a reckless manner the paper's board of directors may already regret; not to mention the fact that for the past three days I have been living in said office, such that now it truly has begun to take on a disorganized or even *crazed* appearance, as Bernice put it this afternoon: *I don't know, Mr. Fitz. I'd lose my head with such a mess, wouldn't be able to find my own brain.*

From my position on the inflatable mattress I can make out the corner windows—rhombuses from this angle—which the half-raised blinds cause to resemble two sleepy pink eyes. The pinkness is due to the stoplight at Main and Cooper. I've watched the light in the room change dozens of times tonight, hundreds of times this week, so I am accustomed to its rhythm, to the fact that in fifty minutes an internal timer mechanism will cause it to begin blinking, which is when the frightening spectral phenomenon that I first encountered by happenstance two nights ago, following the argument with my wife, will appear. This is why I must sleep in Jon's former office and not elsewhere, despite its being filled with bad memories and the mummified stench of cigarette smoke. (He'd refused to cut back once his health began to fail him, and in fact he was smoking as he admitted to me his intentions to retire, pulling me into his office as though we were going to have one of our usual chats—even then he was puffing his Pall Malls conspiratorially, exhaling a theatrical gust of smoke before the key phrases: *doctor more or less ordered, more time with my family, recommended you, best man for the job, not doing you any favors.* Nothing about the money trouble, of course. I didn't make that discovery until later, when I was tasked with cleaning out not just his precarious ashtrays but also the files and computer in his office, and I stumbled upon—or rather, reluctantly deduced over several long, withering days—the damning evidence. And rather than present it to the board, as perhaps I should have done, I actually phoned him up—just two days before his death—and asked about the money. He fumbled at some sort of explanation: *not what it looks like, something I've been meaning to tell you, I've been piecing together.* Then he stopped returning any calls, because he was dead, leaving me to look out his office windows for an explanation that would never come. Is it so outrageous to consider this to be the sort of proverbial unfinished business so common in paranormal lore?)

My watch reads twenty minutes past midnight. As the stoplight changes and washes the room in green, I turn my head back to the carpet, whose effect of appearing blue at a distance yet multihued up close reminds me of a standard cathode-ray-tube television on which seemingly fluid and uniform moving images—a woman's screaming mouth, say, or the furrowed eyebrows of Craig T. Nelson—on closer inspection reveal themselves to be constructed of intricate mosaics of identical red, blue, and green rectangles. Thousands of these tesserae interlock to form a smooth image via simple gestalt principles familiar to any student of psychology. My carpet's mosaic does not, of course, regularly present such images, although in a sense this would be possible—say, if the carpet were an intentionally patterned tapestry. Such eyebrows might conceivably emerge out of some planned pointillism on the part of the carpet manufacturer. A client—a megalomaniacal boss, say—might even request of the manufacturer a tapestry featuring not just his eyebrows but his entire face to adorn an office floor so that every day he'd tread over his own stern visage. Although obviously that would be completely insane. In the light of day, at least, my office carpet projects only the familiar piebald blueness. What's more, for the carpet to further manifest or "televise" moving images, its component fibers (beige, rust, etc.) would have to be not constant in number and brilliance, but *fluctuating,* like the red-blue-green rectangles that become visible on a TV only when one stands close to its bulbous glass screen, and which are created by the passage of three electron beams through a gridded mask, comparable here to the hidden plastic grid that forms the backing of inexpensive carpet panels. No, the carpet has no such dynamism, no explicable properties of movement—a wild carpet that'd be! For it is a TV's fluctuating components that create the dynamic brick-like or mosaic effect that, as one backs slowly away from the television screen, is smoothed by the limits of our visual acuity at the usual viewing distance several feet away. I do find it fascinating that, in a supremely complicated version of the carpet's *blueness*, these few nodes of color are responsible for such diverse emergent images as *frown* or *Craig T. Nelson eyebrow*. I have often planted my face up against the set in our bedroom—the bedroom Mandy and I have shared for twenty years—in order to reassure myself that this is still the case, and I experience unmitigated pleasure in those moments when my eyes breach the acuity threshold and are able to deconstruct a televised image into its constituent atoms. And when I bend over far enough to identify the component colors of the "blue" carpet in my office, I again experience this strange, unmitigated pleasure. I find it oddly relaxing, and, as my stress levels have lately increased, I've been at the screen more often, putting nose to glass and experiencing the beauty of gestalt properties for a few minutes each night. It is not bizarre or *creepy*; rather it is a sort of meditation, little different from the widely accepted practice of gazing out one's office window.

And yet this behavior was precisely the cause of the fight with Mandy, or I should say it precipitated the large and (for us) unprecedentedly vicious fight that exiled me to this unorthodox bedroom. Mandy was used to my spending a few hours each night relaxing in front of the television, but had apparently never seen me engaged in my regular defocusing exercise. I hadn't been hiding the hobby, at least not consciously, but she was nevertheless shocked when she found me that night. She gasped and shouted something like *Are you all right?* in reaction to the sight of me squatting there, in front of the television set, back arched, nose pressed to the screen, and a piece of floss hanging from my mouth. (I'd threaded the floss around a tooth moments before a particularly intricate shade of green appeared on-screen, and I'd rushed to examine its makeup without considering how the floss would add a certain disheveled quality to my appearance if someone were to walk in just then, as Mandy did.) She said she thought I was *having a stroke*. And though I tried to defend the innocence of the activity by comparing it to the widely accepted practice et cetera, she remained shaken. This led to a conversation not about gestalt properties, as one might expect, but about certain changes in my behavior these last few months, behaviors connected in her mind by nothing more than their so-called *creepiness*. She argued that I should *never have taken Jon up* on his recommendation to the board, that my promotion to editor-in-chief, far from increasing our standard of living, was obviously *decreasing our standard of living*, and would no doubt lead to a heart attack or some sort of *mental breakdown*. That instead of *improving our life* the promotion was sure to end up *completely destroying our life*. And the harbingers to this supposed breakdown and life destruction were all of the *creepy* behaviors she now counted on the fingers of one hand, behaviors including (index) the abnormal posture and proximity to screen in my TV-watching habits, discovered by her only that night; (middle) certain prolonged silences she had noticed, which were paradoxically coupled with (ring) volatile emotions, such as anger or frustration, even rage, which contradicted or belied my formerly stoic personality and mimicked my predecessor's own unstable moods; and finally (pinky) a newfound reluctance to discuss any matters relating to *Midweek*. She recounted these so-called creepy behaviors calmly, as though she'd been rehearsing the speech, but despite this show of neutrality, I could feel throughout the bedroom the sheer viciousness of her feelings toward me. Maybe, I suggested, she didn't understand the stress that naturally accompanied my new position, and should talk to Jon's wife, or rather widow, for a better understanding of how to support a beleaguered editor-in-chief of a husband. Surely Jon's widow would prefer an occasionally stressed or beleaguered or even *creepy* editor-in-chief/husband to a *dead editor-in-chief/husband*. Or did she, Mandy, *prefer a dead editor-in-chief to a live one*? We went back and forth like this, moving from bedroom to kitchen and back, and at a certain point Mandy began to softly cry, which so upset me that I left, also crying, and I only barely had the presence of mind to retrieve the old air mattress we'd used on camping trips in the early years of our marriage. When Mandy called the next day, I lied and told her I'd slept at a hotel, and that I needed a few days to cool off. Of course, I had no intention of going to a hotel, not after the phenomenon of that first sublime, sleepless night. Not after I had reason to suspect that Jon had perhaps *not* left me, his second-in-command, in a hopeless position, abandoned by coworkers and wife alike, had not left me in the paper's hour of need, but had manufactured some intricate form of posthumous communication—something to save us all.

I stare down to where my toes hold up a sagging tent of sheet. One of my more benign recent discoveries is that my office gets chilly at night owing to those rattling windows, which have no curtains, only the sort of cheap plastic venetian blinds whose angle is controlled by a plastic rod on the left-hand side. Twisting the rod causes the louvers to tilt one way or the other, which is the only method I have for adjusting the levels of natural light in the room; the apparatus for raising or lowering the blinds—a white string on the right-hand side—is hopelessly knotted. The blinds thus sit permanently half-raised, exposing my room at night to the alternating, and later blinking pink, light as I am trying to sleep. Moreover, I can't but wonder *why* the strings that control the venetian blinds' height are so knotted: Did Jon never lower his blinds? Did he perhaps intentionally knot the string so as to force permanent light into his office? To what end? When I think back, I find that I can't remember the blinds ever being lowered during his tenure, but then he wasn't the sort of supervisor to spend his day fiddling with louvers. In considering the phenomenon, I can take nothing for granted. Anything in the office might be part of the setup. And I've already learned that I did not know Jon nearly so well as I thought. Certainly I was unaware of the genetic time bomb that was his family's history of cardiovascular disease and early death—not until Jon suffered his fatal heart attack, thereby precipitating all or nearly all of my domestic, vocational, and hauntological problems. My colleagues have surely noticed that my clothes haven't changed since

Monday, and that my face wears the blotched-and-greased look of the ejected husband. I suspect I do appear haunted, in a sense.

Though Mandy didn't mention it during the fight, I wonder whether she thought (when she came into our bedroom and found me there with my face against the screen) that I was hoping to pass through the glass into the televised world inside, as characters sometimes do in cartoons, or in a film I happened to return to a few weeks prior to my promotion, the 1982 horror blockbuster *Poltergeist*. (Here the passage occurs off-screen, which renders the notion not at all cartoonish but eerie and, in an odd reversal of the usual viewing conditions surrounding horror movies, actually more frightening to watch on television than in the movie theater. I remember seeing the film on its release with my newlywed wife and finding it manipulative and emotionally leaden. But when I rented and watched the film alone in our bedroom a few months ago—Jon was still alive then, of course—I had to admit that the depictions of the supernatural were quite disturbing ((especially when I pressed my face against the pixels, the images simultaneously filling and obliterating my vision)) and I have since lost some sleep in replaying its scenes of increasingly destructive spectral pranks, culminating in the abduction of Craig T. Nelson's daughter through the television set—through the portal to the afterlife.) Obviously, I wasn't expecting to physically penetrate the television, but I wouldn't blame Mandy for mistaking my nose-against-screen activity as any number of things, just as I wouldn't blame someone for believing my office's carpet to be uniformly blue. I would not fault anyone for what are ultimately automatic, interpretive processes of the mind, and though I have been unable to bear a discussion of the fight itself, or even hear Mandy's voice for more than a few moments each day while assuring her of my adequate health, I hope that soon I will be able to tell her that I forgive any and all of the interpretive processes of her wonderful mind. I would forgive her anything for a few more of the fine years we've shared.

Buried somewhere beneath the strata of my papered wall is a picture of her on our honeymoon. Just an old keepsake. We spent a week in Las Vegas, and in the picture Mandy is leaning against the base of a model of the Eiffel Tower, maybe four stories tall. I'm not sure if this tourist destination still stands in the inconstant skyline of the Vegas strip, and I admit there's something tacky about such a replica, but it's the closest Mandy or I have ever been to Paris, and in the photograph she is visibly happy, one leg bent playfully at the knee. *I've never been so happy*, she even said to me around the time of the picture. I haven't forgotten that. The base of the scale tower is finely gridded and latticed in a truly eye-catching way—the tower's shrunken size creates an even finer texture of grid than on the full-size original—such that focusing on a particular spot in the latticework brings patterns and shapes to the mind's eye. While the structure of the tower does not change, the principles of visual perception are such that my seeing of it does. It was on this trip, perhaps even on the occasion of the photograph, that Mandy, a psychology major at the time, taught me that the phenomenon of finding faces in random or unstructured stimuli is known as pareidolia. She mentioned the case, well-known at the time, of a woman in New Mexico who had seen Jesus's face in a tortilla, prompting thousands to undertake a pilgrimage to her house. Some people—the religious or paranormally inclined, for instance—are particularly susceptible to it, Mandy said. Although she added that the most common case of pareidolia was neither paranormal nor religious, was rather the universally recognized *man in the moon*, which is not visible tonight, or at least not from my vantage on the office floor. After that vicious fight two nights ago, once I'd packed the air mattress and retreated to the office, I found that my thoughts were racing uncontrollably. I kept replaying moments of the argument over and over in my head. To induce sleep, I employed the same method I'd used to relax in front of *Poltergeist*, except instead of staring at the television set, I stared at the carpet. Whereas previously I had attempted to see into *Poltergeist*'s cellular mosaic, into the television's constituent atoms, now I attempted to see into *blueness*'s mosaic, into the carpet's constituent atoms. I concentrated on the carpet's perceived *blueness* vs. the carpet's objective *piedness* for a few hours, hoping to shut myself off from the world, and from my own mind's racing. And it was this—the meditative unfocusing, which I am doing just now in the appropriate way—that allowed me to discover the phenomenon. A phenomenon that I strongly suspect is not meaningless or hallucinogenic or man-in-the-moon pareidolic at all, but which does depend on my knowledge of emergence and gestalt properties. It can be no coincidence that I am in this office and none other, and that these messages have appeared to me, Harold Fitz, someone whose interests very much include the gestalt and pareidolic. I am even beginning to think that it is no coincidence that the window's blinds are stuck at half-mast—not only giving a sleepy appearance to the room's corner face but also enforcing the presence of low, reddish light in the room at night—or that the carpet pops in and out in such a *seemingly* randomized way. It may be no coincidence that the light and temperature are so finely controlled, that a wind worries constantly across my face, that each hypnotic shadow is placed just so. For all I know, these may also be necessary conditions for the phenomenon. In other words, the knotted cords may be *intentionally* knotted. The carpet may be *intentionally* mislaid. The order, the form, the texture of the office may constitute for the initiated some representation of its former owner—the office itself a coded message, waving at me as surely as the pages of my papered wall.

I was thinking about this intricate tissue of effects today when Bernice came into the office without knocking to hand me the daily wire-service summaries, and to discuss the matter of her most recent paycheck, which had bounced. Jon's ancient and perhaps eternal secretary—now the office secretary by order of the board of directors—appeared in the doorframe to ask whether there wasn't some *reasonable explanation* for the *obviously a mistake, Mr. Fitz*. And while I assured her that it must be nothing, in my head I knew it was not nothing. I asked that she not read anything into what was really just an accident, a meaningless data point, but I myself was reading furiously into what was clearly a meaningful data point, the ultimate data point, the point that pointed directly at both Jon and (by proxy, since I'd been suppressing the evidence of his embezzlement) me. And what's worse,

Bernice replied—croaking in that half-dead voice of hers—was that she'd already emailed the board to alert them of her concerns, and *hoped I wouldn't mind*. To which I said *no*, while indeed thinking *yes*, for I did mind. Maybe I should have raged at her, as Jon would have. Maybe I did rage. Maybe, because I did not rage, or raged only a little, it appeared as though I was haunted by guilt. Maybe Bernice had already surmised that Jon and I had worked together, chief and assistant, to cook the books for our personal gain, or even that I had done it all under Jon's nose. Could I disprove it, I wondered as she shuffled out the door, her back hunched and her entire bearing like that of the shadowy medium who interprets the paranormal event in *Poltergeist* once the family has finally accepted the existence of their eponymous haunters. So I was forced to accept Jon's embezzlement, even though it made no sense to me, and still makes no sense. The importance of tonight's defocusing exercise was thus brought home as Bernice left the office, shutting the door so that it startled the thumbtacked papers. It was at once clearer than ever, as I was overwhelmed by the scene framed in the window, as tears collected in my tear ducts, that my studies in emergent properties—such as *blueness* or *Craig T. Nelson eyebrowness*—had been necessary steps toward learning to see the coded message in the office, a message I believe, with increasing certainty, is the remainder or shade of Jon Friedman, come to confess his crimes, and to show me the way out from under them.

Ah—I've just remembered something. Earlier tonight, I imagined that the Nelson family's young daughter crawls into the glass-paned eye of a television set, crossing that threshold into the realm of the undead. But on just now espying the small supply closet in the corner of my office, I am reminded that this moment of television penetration is not just off-screen, but nonexistent. In fact, I'd constructed the imagined scene out of other textual and paratextual elements of the film. (First, the movie poster, which depicts a young girl sitting in front of a television, her hands flat against the screen as though she might pass into it. ((Incidentally, one tagline for the film—*They're here*—is written just above the television, while another—*It knows what scares you*—appears below the film's title. This has always seemed strange to me: that the poltergeist(s) of the film is/are referred to as both singular and plural entities, on the one hand *they* but on the other hand *it*, as though a poltergeist might shift or increase in identity in a way so contra to our understanding of objects that our grammar cannot consistently describe it/them.)) And second, the film's off-screen abduction of the girl into the spirit world, which takes place in the children's *closet*, not via TV, and which is a rather more pedestrian horror-movie trope. The abduction-via-TV was my mind's own gestalt, a conflation of suggestive elements surrounding my memories of the film.) It is also creepily true that the images on a television are not, ontologically speaking, really there: when I watch *Poltergeist*, Craig T. Nelson is as spectral as—is no less a blocky mosaic than—the supernatural beings who haunt him. Since the phenomenon first appeared two nights ago, I have quelled my fears by imagining that I am just such a Nelsonian patriarch, composed of courageous bricks, confronting the unknown for the sake of my family: for Mandy. I would redeem myself in her eyes, would make her reconsider the cruel, flat intonation of her voice as she washed the dishes and sat across from me at the kitchen table, staring straight ahead and turning a coffee cup around on a napkin, twisting brown rings into the white, uttering the trivially true cliché *not the person I married*.

I glance at my office door, which is able to shut until only a sliver of space remains between the door and jamb, but cannot form a complete seal—with the click of the knob's tongue entering the door's mouth—due to a tectonic ridge of carpet that juts out over the thinner strips lining the hallway. The backward C of the door's silhouette casts rippled striations across the blinking—yes, at last blinking—glow of the streetlight. The blinking bathes the room in urgent periods of dark pink. Supernatural beings are commonly thought to have an *urgent message* for the living that they/it mean(s) to communicate. Perhaps Jon will show me the location of a written confession, or some other piece of incontrovertible proof that I could take to the board. A piece of evidence explaining that I had nothing to do with the paper's imminent, unavoidable demise. Or perhaps the embezzlement was indeed part of *something big*, some paper-saving scheme the details of which Jon (the shade of Jon, through the portal of an office Jon erected before his death) means to inform me. Not that I have any way of knowing how closely my own experiences approximate the ontology of those fictional worlds. In this world, at least, what happens first is an unnatural darkening of the light around the doorframe—just like this—like slowly steeping tea water, and a reddening of the already pinkish objects in the room—

Yes, it's happening: the carpet has begun to bubble.

Bubbling is the nearest word for it: this shifting mass at once unified and composed of discrete atoms, the way I imagine water molecules would look in a simmering pot if we could see them. The carpet roils, it seethes, embodying the sea-like depth anticipated in miniature by its molehills and pied blueness. I am awake on my raft of air, eyes locked on the now truly three-dimensional carpet. Globs of carpet matter bubble and shimmer, forming ripples and waves, moving in a way that would seem to mimic not only water but, if I were several feet farther away, the electric tempest of television static. It is a movement of carpet and a movement of figures in the carpet. (On the first night, I was convinced this movement was unreal, that it was akin to the illusory popping of Mandy's mini–Eiffel Tower shapes. If I focused my eyes on the door held ajar or on the nearby wastebasket, I could even convince myself that all was yet a static pied blue beneath me. But the movement returned, in strengthening waves, until my vision could not but classify it as authentic. By now—my third night with the phenomenon—I am primed to recognize it as real.) The variance of the fabric colors, the areas that are predominantly cerulean, or salt and pepper, are now morphing into discrete shapes, becoming curves and blobs and round eyes and, mostly, yawning or screaming mouths. On first encountering them, I'd hoped that perhaps I'd been sitting too close to the TV all those months, and that my vision was now permanently seared with the texture of its flickering cathodes. That old wives' tale briefly envenomed my doubts two nights ago. But no, they are mouths.

There can be no denying these horrifying mouths. The very *mouthness* of the mouths proves that a higher-order dissonance must be at work, that I am either flat-out hallucinating or else can believe what I'm seeing. Some of the mouths have teeth. Some are toothless and lipless, just widening globules. Some have impossibly long teeth, like fingers. Some of the lips are split in the middle, causing the unusual sight of a four-lipped mouth, grotesque and rectangular. Some of the mouths seem to be singing. But most take on a permanent fixed shape associated in my mind with a "bloodcurdling" type of scream. They seem to be increasing in number, not by mitosis but by steadily displacing the areas of shapeless bubbling. After some minutes—ten, I'd guess, although time passes strangely once I am transfixed by their number and variety, all other thoughts displaced by a keen awareness of mouths (I even touch my own mouth, absentmindedly)—the floor is densely covered in mouths. They exclaim no message, only wiggle and bump *creepily*, as Mandy would say, and worm against one another. What happens now—and I am expecting it this time—is that the mouths themselves, in addition to singing and screaming and worming, begin actually to bubble in the same way that the carpet itself had bubbled. They form larger, multimouth shapes. Whereas previously the individual fibers of the carpet had served as the atoms of shape and movement, now the mouths themselves are the monadic components of higher-order bubbling. As I watch this for the third time, it occurs to me that I already know that any attempt to record these mouths on photograph or film would be fruitless, that the phenomenon depends precisely on my particular seeing of it, that in some sense it is illusory, a conspiracy between the mouths and myself, as contingent on my own perception of it as a Magic Eye print or hologram. Yes, what the bubbling most resembles is a spooky room-size hologram. Yet it feels no less real for that. All during its transformation the room is silent, save for the occasional squeak of my body shifting against the vinyl surface of the mattress.

What eventually forms from the mouths is a giant, room-size face. A face made of mouths. And though the mouth-face is ultimately made of carpet, is virtually in the carpet, at the same time it appears to hover above the carpet by several inches, an effect that my brain struggles to resolve. The face alternates between two shades of purple as the red streetlight blinks and bleeds over the carpet's bubbling blue. Its eyes float just below the wastebasket; its chin bucks and breaks against the working wall. The face is longer than I am tall and anamorphically distorted owing to my low angle of observation. Yet I can see that the skin drapes a little over each eye in the epicanthic way of lifelong smokers. The mouth is a narrow, unbending mouth, bled of all thickness, lacking the hunter's bow shape of the upper lip. When the face has settled on this permutation—its exact features vary from night to night, as an artist's sketches approach what will be the final painting, and tonight he looks even more like Jon than in previous iterations—when the features have fully solidified and the atomic mouths are shrunk to near-points, the chin quivers, the mouth cracks, and the face starts to speak.

He emits no sound, but the lips move in a way that I might read them. To get a better view of the mouth, though, I must stand up on the air mattress, and it was my fumbling while undertaking just this maneuver that previously caused the face and mouths to dissipate, communication to end, and the room to resolve into its familiar, unshaded features. What's more, I am afraid—terrified, even—of accidentally losing my balance and stepping onto the face, into the seething mouths. What would crossing this threshold feel like? I am reminded not just of the cartoonish conceit of passing through the glass lens of a television (which I earlier mistook for an abduction scene in *Poltergeist*), but of the fact that the specters in *Poltergeist* do indeed pass out through the television, across the screen, into reality. Would contact with the face(s) somehow enable it/them to cross a similar threshold, into the corporeal world? Would my foot set loose the roiling mass of mouths, the seething static of mouths that now seems to me less like a holographic projection of the carpet than like a threshold left ajar, a world straining at its dimensions, near to bursting? Would I be abducted if I were to step into this sea? I think of Mandy, how distraught she'd be at my disappearance, how she'd worry that she was at fault, or that I'd abandoned her. How she would resign herself only slowly to widowhood over months and years. Widowhood would emerge, I think, with painful turgidity, as each day she expected my return a little less.

And yet I will stand. I must find out what it—he—they—want(s), whether mine is some bedlamitical theory of Jon's cryptic final call, or whether my life does hang on a final, muddled message from beyond. Whether Jon had indeed arranged the office before his death to effect such phenomena, pulling at corners of the carpet to form contours, knotting the cords of the venetian blinds, maniacally adjusting the flow of light into the room, conducting ritual preparations to prepare for his specter's return. I am beset by the impulse: I must rise now.

Just lifting my head from the mattress—slowly, so as to disturb nothing—takes more than a minute, and it strikes me how these stilted movements would appear to an observer as *creepy*; fearful of disturbing the dead, I move with the very slowness of death. Slowly I turn so that my knees and hands are against the mattress, so that if I were over the face, we might even look into each other's unblinking eyes. The mattress presents issues of balance exacerbated by the fearful wobble in my legs. My limbs push four parabolic depressions into the bladder of air beneath me. As I rise onto one knee and then off it (this process taking several agonizing minutes), my feet press suddenly deeper into the slack fabric than expected and, for a terrible moment, I almost pitch forward onto the floor—onto the churning face. At the last instant I manage to steady myself with one hand on the desk so that I am tripodded over the mattress. My torso and head really do now lean over the face, just as the streetlight blinks and submerges the floor, the room, the face, in dark pink—the precise shade of pink as the otherworldly mucus in which the returned abductees find themselves covered at the climax of the film, as mother and child return from the world of the dead, reborn from death, the fluid—I only now realize—an afterbirth of the dead, an afterdeath.

But this is new. Unlike on previous nights, the face does not bubble back *into* the carpet, dissipating as an image does into television static. No, the goopy pink face grows startlingly clear from this angle. And as I gaze down, towering above the face, as I become a tower with a face above the face, I can at last read its lips. The face is *saying my name.* I can make out the familiar biting of Jon's lower lip that precedes an *f* sound, followed by a scrunching of the entire lower half of the face: the *tz.* Yes, the mouth shapes must correspond to "ftz"—they repeat in that order, the face intoning "ftz ftz ftz." It is the familiar shape of my name, which I hear in my head as Jon would have said it, exploding in midrage or racked with depression. My own face (which I again feel with my hands) reflects the hovering face beneath me, Jon's face, as I speak along with him, my throat tightening, my voice giving volume to the silent mouth below: *ftz ftz ftz Fitz Fitz Fitz.* I tower for some inconceivable period of time, whispering my name until the word loses its meaning—that is to say, until its properties dissolve into morphemes and then meaningless spittle, until the properties of *sounding like* and *meaning* are effaced, rubbed down to sound and then mouth shapes that mean nothing, sound like nothing, signify nothing, and the mouth has worked cruelly into a smile, its expulsions transformed into what is almost like laughter, horrible bursts of gay, meaningless laughter, and I know what I am being told, and my feet tingle above the ground, floating, in a sense, like the face—I am, after all, suspended atop a bubble of air in the office that is mine—and I grasp the desk firmly, as though aloft over a great sea.

About the Author

B.D. MAUK lives in Berlin, where he is a Fulbright research scholar. He has written online and in print for the *New Yorker*, the *Believer*, the *Los Angeles Review of Books*, and elsewhere.

BEAUTY SECRETS

JAMESON FITZPATRICK

Never get fat or old: let's begin
with the obvious. Smoking's glamorous
—until your first wrinkle, that is.

There will never be a new black.
If you're walking away, better look
best from the back. For rosy cheeks

and devil-may-care hair, try facing
into the wind on the way to tell him
I'm sorry, it's finished. A window

reflection's no substitute for a compact
but will do in a pinch. Learn how
to look bored and how to look

interested and when to look to which.
Never lie by more than an inch.
Master the art of barely parted lips:

the just-so prelude to O, mouth open
just enough for him to imagine it full.
In conversation each lull's a chance

to stretch and show off your neck, its long
pale appeal belying the blood underneath.
Only smile if you've got good teeth.

And if, like me, you look prettiest in fall—
make the most of those few months,
then don't leave your bed at all.

About the Author

JAMESON FITZPATRICK is the author of the chapbook *Morrisroe: Erasures* (89plus/LUMA Publications), and holds an MFA from New York University, where he also teaches. His poems have appeared or are forthcoming in the *American Reader*, the *Awl*, the *Literary Review*, and *Poetry*, among elsewhere.

Jameson on Writing
"Beauty Secrets"

Dorothy Parker. I've always admired Parker's poems for their music and sly wit, for how deftly she can turn a phrase to reveal what's both terrible and terribly funny about human nature and experience. I began this poem deep in a rereading of Parker's *Complete Poems*, and it certainly owes a debt to the incisive rhyme of poems like "News Item."

Lana Del Rey. In addition to enjoying her songs, I've been fascinated by Lana Del Rey's cultural reception—which has been so dominated by questions about artifice and "pose." I read her coquettish persona and lyrical preoccupations (with clothes, makeup, etc.) as calculatedly coy, at once embracing and subverting the trope of the beautiful-but-troubled female singer. I'd say "Beauty Secrets" has a similar aim.

Cosmopolitan. In middle school and early high school, my girlfriends and I (strictly platonic, of course—I was avowedly gay even then) used to spend hours poring over magazines like *Cosmopolitan.* Though I think I was able to recognize the absurdity of some of that beauty advice even then, I also internalized plenty: I'll still read any and every article promising the secret to perfect skin. And the snappy language of magazine copy was a stylistic inspiration, of course.

My own habits. Plenty of the details in this poem are (embarrassingly) autobiographical. I, for example, *do* feel more attractive when I'm walking into the wind, am constantly checking my reflection in store windows, and, as I'm self-conscious about my teeth, almost never smile in photographs.

Judith Butler's *Gender Trouble*. Like a vast number of liberal arts students in the past two decades, this book was my introduction to the theory of gender performativity, which solidified my understanding of sex and gender as social constructs. As a gay man on the "fem" end of the spectrum, Butler's work has also been of great personal significance, helping me to claim my place in a broader culture that's constantly policing gender transgression—and giving me the freedom to write into the "fem," as I do in this poem.

Keith Carter © 2013

Keith Carter © 2013

CAT MAN

HEATHER MONLEY

Grace meets Roger at a small party held by mutual friends. She isn't a particularly superstitious person, but she believes she can tell in the first moments of meeting someone if they're going to be important in her life. She feels this way when she first sees Roger, his nose buried deep in the fur of a long-haired cat.

Grace enjoys the company of animals, but generally feels that public affection should be limited to calm petting and perhaps extend as far as holding the animal in one's arms. More involved displays—nuzzling, saying sweet nothings in a high voice—should occur only when no one is around to observe. But it's clear she's stumbled upon Roger in a private moment. Walking through the bedroom door to leave her coat on the bed, she finds him cradling Toughy—the long-haired cat—and murmuring something like, "Pretty boy—pretty, pretty kitty." Roger notices Grace and sets the cat gently on the floor, but he does not seem the least bit embarrassed. His glasses have slipped askew, and he adjusts them with an assured, fluid motion. Grace forms an idea of Roger's character: He's confident in his actions, unapologetic, but also kindhearted. He's the sort of person Grace admires, the kind she wishes she could emulate.

"You like cats," Grace says.

Roger answers, "Yes."

"You have one?"

"No."

Grace communicates mild surprise, and Roger smiles. "Not the right time in my life, I'm afraid."

They've walked down the hall, back into the party, and someone starts speaking to Roger. Grace wanders off. The rest of the night—when she sees him across the room or recognizes his voice among others—she feels a small, itching interest that she hasn't yet identified, but she can't find an excuse to speak to him again. It's possible she'll never see him after tonight. But then she's in the kitchen searching for a bottle opener, and Roger appears. He has overheard her talking about her apartment hunt, and tells her that he's looking for a new roommate.

Roger's apartment will likely be too expensive for Grace. He is, she estimates, a few years older than she is, and he's wearing a collared shirt of good quality tucked into jeans, the casual outfit of a well-established young professional. Grace is in her early twenties, and moved to New York a few months before the party. She'd had loose plans of pursuing a music career while working a day job on the side, but hasn't found success in either pursuit. Working at the box office of a music venue a few days a week, she makes little money, not enough to keep up with her rent. Her roommates have told her that she'll have to move out. She doesn't tell Roger any of this.

Grace drinks more than she'd planned to. As she's leaving the party, she passes Roger in the hall and says, "Good night, cat man."

"Excuse me?" he says.

Explaining what she means—about the moment with Toughy and the bedroom and the coats—Grace feels embarrassed, especially as she notices that she's interrupted Roger's conversation with a woman. He is leaning against the wall, and the two are standing close. And though Roger smiles when Grace explains the joke, actually seems relieved to understand what she's referring to, Grace goes home imagining that he will now politely avoid her inquiries about the apartment. She wonders if he's going home with that woman. But by the time she wakes up the next morning, he has already sent her an email.

Roger lives in a Brooklyn neighborhood that Grace admires. At his suggestion, they meet at a coffeehouse near his apartment. Roger is dripping wet because it's raining and he hasn't bothered to bring an umbrella. The apartment is close, he says, and he's sure the rain will let up before they leave. He shrugs, but Grace can tell by the way he keeps shaking and squeezing at his damp clothes that the wetness makes him uncomfortable.

Roger is chubbier than Grace remembered, but not unattractive. She imagines women calling him cuddly. He asks about her job, and she tells him about the music venue, adding that she's looking for something more full-time. Roger nods, smiles, laughs when appropriate. He tells her about the apartment, the neighborhood, says it would be great if she took the room because he wants a roommate he can trust. He names the rent. It's surprisingly low. Grace almost asks, "Are you sure?" but holds back. She doesn't want him to change his mind.

The coffee shop is muffin-themed, and all the food—even that completely unrelated to muffins—is forced to involve muffins in some way. Grace orders a muffin salad, which turns out to be an ordinary salad with a savory cheese muffin on the side. She eats half the muffin and offers the rest to Roger, who spears it with a fork, leaning in close and smiling as if they are coconspirators.

"You know," Roger says, "how cats knead people with their claws? When they're purring? Another name for that is making muffins."

They walk a couple of blocks to the apartment. The rain has not let up, and they huddle together under Grace's umbrella. So close to him, Grace can smell food on his breath when he laughs. It's not a sour or unpleasant smell; rather, sweet and bready, something reminiscent of home or childhood. When they enter the building, Roger hesitates at the bottom of the stairs and their eyes meet. He looks away and laughs. "So wet," he says as he removes his jacket and shakes it. Drops of water splat on the tile.

The apartment is on the second floor and is not very large but is light and pleasant inside, simply decorated with a few houseplants and black-and-white photographs of innocuous landscapes. Grace sees nothing related to cats except an odd porcelain figurine high on a bookshelf. The bedroom that will be hers doesn't have a closet, but the previous roommate has left behind a fiberboard wardrobe. Though the rent is cheaper, this apartment is far nicer than the dark and cramped one where Grace currently lives in the far northern reaches of Manhattan. There, the lock on the front door is broken, and Grace sometimes finds homeless people asleep in the lobby.

She doesn't hesitate: she tells Roger she'll take it.

Before moving in, she gets a call from him. He remembers that she's looking for a job, and a position has opened at his organization. Roger works, Grace learns, in the communications department of a well-known nonprofit. The position is temporary, but could be extended to a permanent job if they like her work. Grace applies and gets it. Roger had put in a good word for her.

She starts work immediately—answering phones, photocopying, filling out spreadsheets. She works in a different department from Roger, and on her first day, she sees him only once. He is walking quickly, talking to a colleague and carrying a folder heavy with white paper. He smiles and makes a flurried gesture, as if to say that he would like to talk but is on his way to a meeting.

She doesn't see Roger again until she moves into the apartment, at which point she finds that he maintains certain privacies. To avoid walking down the hall in a towel after showering, he changes his clothes in the bathroom. When she finds him reading on the couch, he hugs the book close to his chest so that she can't read the title.

But once, having just come home from work, Roger leaves his bedroom door open as he changes his shirt, and Grace, walking down the hall to the kitchen, sees him. His chest is covered in fine black hairs, but Grace, who generally prefers a smoother torso, finds his oddly attractive. She notices herself, after this incident, glancing toward his bedroom door, and listening to the sound of water running while he showers. Grace doesn't like to think of herself as the kind of person who would do anything so awkward as to sleep with her roommate, but then again, she believes she's an open-minded person, and doesn't entirely rule the idea out.

Grace seeks out small details to expand her understanding of Roger. She notes a medicinal scent in the bathroom, and in the living room, an old roll-top desk, nicked in several places so that a light wood shows through the dark stain. On a bookcase are two shelves of self-help books. "I used to feel lost," Roger explains.

Next to the bookshelf is a glass case displaying tiny models of buildings. Roger tells Grace they're an old hobby of his. She leans in close. They're made out of paper: tiny castles and important buildings from around the world. Roger has labeled them: *Taj Mahal, Mount Vernon.* They are coated in thin dust. He explains that he doesn't make these anymore, that he's lost interest in buildings. "Enormous examples of people pretending to be civilized."

Now, he places in her hand a model of the Centre Pompidou. She feels the delicate edges, the careful work Roger has performed with knives and glue. It gives her a strange and intimate thrill.

Most evenings, Roger stays late at the office, and Grace has an hour or so to herself. She goes to her wardrobe, removes a dull brown case, and straps an accordion over her shoulders. Heavy notes fill the apartment. A casual listener would deem her playing skillful, but the instrument is still fairly new to her. She doesn't want Roger to hear. She plays only ten minutes before switching to guitar, a quieter instrument and less eccentric. Ten minutes of accordion here and there will not allow her to improve, and this worries Grace.

She expects to find more time to practice on weekends, when she supposes Roger will have plans with friends, but as the weekends pass, she finds that he socializes less than she would expect of someone with his confidence and charm. If she goes out in the evening, she imagines he has done the same, and when she returns, she listens for the sound of a woman's voice coming from his bedroom. In the mornings, she expects to find a woman in the kitchen, a woman with long smooth legs, a woman who will be making coffee and wearing one of Roger's shirts. But no such person ever appears. Instead, on these mornings, Roger walks into the kitchen alone, and when Grace asks him what he did the night before, she learns he stayed home. "Independence and solitude are part of my nature," he says with a shrug, as if this were a sentence that could be uttered casually.

Grace starts staying home with him. When friends call, she finds herself making excuses. She and Roger cook dinner together and watch movies and have long conversations. She plays her guitar for him (though not her accordion) and he responds with enthusiasm. In a matter of only a few weeks, her life begins to revolve around him, and she lives according to his advice. When he smells cigarette smoke on her clothes and suggests healthier ways of relieving stress, she quits smoking and takes up jogging. She feels comfortable following his advice. These changes in her life have all been positive.

They live together six weeks before they have sex. They are sitting on the couch, watching a television drama, and Grace leans her head on his shoulder. He strokes her hair. Grace's heart beats hard and she almost stops breathing. His hand runs over her arm, and then his lips are against hers. They are half-undressed when they move to his bedroom. She is on top of him, then he is on top of her, and she can't stop kissing him, as if his mouth has something she needs but can't quite get. She slips her hand over his back, which like his chest is covered with hair, but the hair isn't coarse—rather, very soft. She slips her hand slowly down and when it comes to just above his butt, she feels a hard, bony bump.

She draws her hand back fast. They carry on, but Grace is distracted. Roger must know she felt the thing, and yet he behaves as if nothing has happened. And then it's over, and they're lying next to each other in bed, and Roger says, "It's a tail."

"Excuse me?"

"I'm growing a tail."

Grace has never heard of anyone growing a tail—perhaps infants born with unwanted appendages, but a tail growing on an adult? She doesn't know what to say and ventures, "I'm sorry."

Roger smiles. "I want the tail. It's something I want."

This is when Roger tells Grace that he is turning himself into a cat.

———

Grace wakes early the next morning, in her own bed. When she hears the first stirrings in Roger's room, the creak of him turning on the mattress, she pulls a hat over her unwashed hair and heads out the door.

Outside it's wet and unpleasant. Old women wrapped in coats carry heavy loads of groceries. Their steps are impossibly slow. Grace takes the train into Manhattan and, despite the weather, heads to the park. It is early December and the last leaves are brown and falling. Few people have ventured out today, so if Grace's face betrays emotion—not to say it necessarily does—no one sees. Occasional shadowy figures keep their heads down as they pass. Grace weaves around the paths for an hour before she decides she's too wet and cold to continue, and she leaves the park and heads to the art museum, where the slightest donation will allow her entry to a place that is dry and reasonably warm. She finds herself first in a special exhibit featuring an eighteenth-century painter, a man who devoted his practice to portraits of a monarch's private menagerie. But leopards, tigers, and lions feel too close to home, and Grace moves on to safer subjects. She spends several hours in rooms of eighteenth- and nineteenth-century portraits, admiring minute details of women's costumes: the ribbons, the ruffles, the changes in corset shape.

At last, Grace gets on the subway and heads home. She feels calmer, full of reason. Changing into a cat is impossible, and what evidence does she have? Roger's body hair is oddly prodigious and soft, and she did feel a strange protuberance in the place where a tail might be, but she hasn't actually seen this tail. It could be anything. A prosthesis, perhaps.

As the train rumbles through its tunnels, the previous night's conversation replays in her head. At first she'd thought Roger was joking, but he'd insisted with great earnestness. He had realized that he needed to live the rest of his life as a cat, and then he had learned it was possible.

"Like a sex change," Grace had said at last, biting at a corner of her lip.

Roger scoffed. What was a sex change—surgery on a couple key places, a regimen of hormones—compared to his own transformation? Every inch of his body would change—every limb, every organ. He would no longer walk on two legs. He'd no longer speak. He would cease to be human.

As Grace exits the train, she shivers. Roger must be delusional. She'll have to find a new apartment.

But then, walking home from the station, she passes vintage clothing stores and the muffin-themed coffeehouse, and a restaurant packed with people with attractive hairstyles. It's a charming neighborhood, she thinks, and her rent is so very low. She remembers her old apartment, with the broken lock and the men asleep on the lobby floor.

She'll stay in the apartment, but she and Roger will be no more than roommates. What happened last night—that will never happen again.

Grace pauses at the door to the building. The rain has turned to something approximating snow, a slushy mix that half floats, half plummets. She watches it fall in the glow of the streetlamps. It's close enough to snow—the first of the winter—for Grace to find it beautiful.

———

Roger explains that he is achieving his transformation through a combination of medication and mental exercises, a regimen he has cobbled together through extensive research. Grace has just walked in from work to find him already home and seated at the coffee table, which he has covered in books and stacks of paper. She has learned today, as Roger predicted, that her temp job has been extended to a permanent position. She feels grateful, so she sits beside him. He places a hand on her knee. She gently but firmly removes it.

Roger lifts one of the books from the table, a paperbound journal claiming scientific contents. He wants her to understand that this is real, that changes like his are described in resources that are reputable in appearance. He flips through yellowed pages and holds open an article with the title "On Probable Future Advances in the Mutability of Species." Grace starts to read further, but Roger shuts the book and picks up another.

He flips through countless photocopies, preserved in plastic sleeves. Grace sees pages of tiny print, grainy photographs, and incomprehensible diagrams with dotted lines and arrows. Roger tells her of Soviet experiments, of twentieth-century medical breakthroughs covered up for unclear political reasons, and of ancient tales of alchemy and miracles. Then he picks up a heavy leather-bound book. This, he explains, is his most important reference.

He opens to columns of tiny type. Grace leans in to inspect the text, but finds it beyond her understanding. Though the sentences seem to be written in English, there are too many long and unfamiliar words, in strange syntaxes. Roger explains that understanding the book's teachings has taken him many months—almost two years—of study, and as she can see, his transformation is still in its early stages.

Roger flips through the pages, showing Grace the density of text, the complicated science of which he is master. As he flips, he comes to a section of lithographed images, which he quickly moves past, but Grace stops his hand and turns the pages back so that she can see. The illustrations are of people and animals—cats, dogs, horses, monkeys—but when Grace turns the page, she sees a spread of horrifying in-between things.

Roger snaps the book shut and gathers his resources from the table. He stacks them neatly on the surface of his rolltop desk, then pulls down the cover and locks it with a gentle turn of the key. He turns back to Grace and smiles.

———

Over the following weeks, Grace contemplates breaking into Roger's desk and destroying his books and papers, but worries this might be excessively cruel. The leather-bound volume looks old and rare. It may be quite valuable.

When the holidays come, Grace visits her family in suburban Virginia. She eats mashed potatoes, sings carols, and tries not to think about Roger. But when she unwraps a pair of fluffy black slippers, she imagines Roger's hair growing dense like the faux fur. She thinks about his tail, growing ever imperceptibly longer. Suddenly, the normality around her seems false and unsettling. When she returns to New York and enters the apartment, she feels a small degree of relief. When Roger approaches, she allows him to hug her, but when he moves to kiss her cheek, she steps away.

Grace notes slight alterations in his appearance, though she can't be sure if they occurred in the time she was gone or if it's the shock of seeing him again after being away. He seems to be hairier—furrier—than before, perhaps slightly shorter, and there's something about his eyes that's new and strange.

Roger walks with Grace into the living room and hands her an envelope. Inside is a videotape. *Living with Species Change*, the label reads, *For Family and Friends*. "You don't have to watch now," Roger says, but Grace is curious. He pops the video in, and after a few seconds, warped strains of New Age music pour from the television. People with Australian accents talk about acceptance and new ways of living. These people wear velvet clothing and jewelry of crystals and pentagrams. They offer few specifics, though many note the period of transformation as being more difficult than the completely altered state. Grace waits for the transformed themselves to enter the scene, for a cat to leap onto someone's lap or a rabbit to hop across a coffee table, but the video's population remains strictly human.

The following week, at the office, Grace is delivering a document to another floor and passes a conference room humming with voices. "Birthday party?" she asks a woman leaving the room. The woman is giggling and turning back to wave to a group of laughing coworkers, and hardly seems to hear Grace. "Have some cake," she says, touching her fingertips to Grace's wrist. "It's Roger's last day."

Roger stands in the middle of the room, a forkful of cake midair. He sees Grace and shrugs.

That night, back at the apartment, she asks how he'll support himself. He explains that he's saved up some money he inherited when his father died, and besides, once he's a cat, he'll have fewer expenses. "I can't keep working as if I were human," he says. "I have to act like a cat. Quitting is part of the process."

Roger's absence at work feels heavier than Grace would have expected. Now that he's gone, she understands how comforting it had been, imagining him just one floor above. She leaves the office on her lunch break. It snowed the day before, and Midtown Manhattan is a mess of slushy streets and salt. People crowd in the shadows of monstrous skyscrapers. They hover around kebab carts and trucks selling dumplings, and file into burrito chains and upscale sandwich shops. All these people, in perfectly tailored suits and coats, are forced to fulfill their animal need for food. Humans, Grace thinks, are just a kind of mammal, and suddenly the structure of civilization seems tenuous and fragile. Perhaps Roger is right—perhaps these buildings, these clothes, the lives people lead, are complex forms of denial—and though his reaction is extreme, maybe there's something to it.

The idea burns in her all day. That night, she's cooking with Roger in the cramped space of their kitchen. As they move about, their bodies brush against each other. At one such moment, Grace reaches for Roger's arm and lets her hand caress it before moving away. The next time Roger moves past her, he takes her in his arms.

The following morning, Grace slips from Roger's bed and walks to her own room. She pulls on her bathrobe, then reaches into her wardrobe and pulls out the accordion. She unclasps the case. She has not looked at the instrument in weeks, and she takes a moment to admire its shiny blackness, its mother-of-pearl inlay, before carrying it into the living room. She sits. Her fingers brush against the keys. Then she pulls the instrument out with a breathy heave, and as she pushes in, clear chords fill the room.

The song she plays is simple, not the jaunty polka generally associated with the accordion, but slower, sweeter, somewhat sad. When she looks up, Roger is standing in the doorway. His eyes are closed. He smiles.

Roger rarely leaves the apartment now, and there's little chance anyone will see the two of them together. They allow their relationship to exist in secret. At work, Grace tells her coworkers that Roger has moved to California, that he's working in animal rights, she thinks, but he hasn't kept in touch. The coworkers don't ask many questions, and Grace is amazed at how easily she has created a private life separate from her public one, a true life hidden from the world.

Perhaps it's the warming temperatures that make Grace optimistic, for the winter is melting into spring, and when walking in the park, she notices blossoms appearing on one tree, then another. She imagines walking with Roger in this place, their hands clasped, the sun warming their hair and shoulders. It's not too late, she thinks in such happy moments. Their relationship has not come too late, but at just the right time. Roger might yet change his mind. He might stay human.

It's such moments as these—when she is apart from Roger—that Grace is happiest in their love. When she returns to the apartment, she sees the soft fuzz growing on his face—a fuzz that quickly grows denser, like the hair on the rest of his body. When she looks into his eyes, she finds his irises are larger, and their deep brown tone is shifting toward yellow. His pupils have become just slightly oblong.

Roger's behavior also changes. She comes home from work one day to find him meowing along with a recording of a cat. He rolls around on his back on the living room rug or, in the kitchen, sits on the floor and paws at the dish towels that hang from the oven handle. When she reaches out to him, he bats her hand away. "Sorry," he says. "Just something I'm trying."

On Roger's last excursion from the apartment, for which he shaves the fur from his face and wears dark glasses, the two of them head to the property manager's Park Slope office to sign the lease over to Grace. She learns that she's been paying only a small portion of the total rent, but she and Roger do not discuss this. Next, to the bank, where Roger transfers to her the contents of his savings account. Then Grace takes Roger's hand and points out the sunny weather, suggesting an outing to a park or a walk down tree-lined streets. But Roger seems nervous and turns toward the apartment, from which he'll never emerge again.

Grace can't halt Roger's transformation, and soon his body has changed dramatically. His black fur becomes dense, covering his body. He's noticeably smaller, about Grace's height, and though he still walks on two legs, his posture becomes somewhat hunched, as though his arms want to reach for the floor. His nose flattens, begins to turn up, and his fingers become shorter and the nails sharpen, sometimes leaving scratches when he touches Grace's skin. When they kiss, she must beware his teeth and rough tongue. These changes are off-putting, and when Roger tells Grace that their intimacy is a mental block in his process of transformation, there's hardly a need to say it. They haven't made love for several weeks.

Still, the finality of the statement crushes Grace, and even more so Roger's request that she watch over him once he's a cat. With the lease and bank account in her name, she has gathered that Roger expects this, but now the idea becomes real and terrifying. "It will only be the length of a cat's life," he says, consoling her. "Not a human's." The effect on her emotions is quite the opposite of Roger's intent.

The next morning, Grace again pulls her accordion from its case, again plays a sweet and mournful tune, but this time, Roger is not silent when he joins her in the living room. He sings along in chilling, groaning meows.

"Don't," she says, but Roger meows again.

The accordion returns to its case and does not come out. Grace plays music less and starts reading more—long and intricate nineteenth-century novels in which everything goes wrong, but all ends well for the romantic protagonists.

In June, Roger decides to give up human food, and Grace goes to the pet store. She picks up stainless steel bowls for food and water, and then selects the most expensive cat food, cans with pleasing graphic designs. They claim to be filled with ethical seafood and quality meat from free-range animals. At the register the cashier holds up the bowls and asks, "New kitty?" Grace fiddles with her credit card to avoid meeting the woman's eyes. That night, Grace fills Roger's bowls and sets them on the table, but he says, "No, you should feed me on the floor." He crouches over his food bowl, awkwardly because he is not yet quadrupedal. As he eats the food, he forces a smile and says, "Delicious."

Roger speaks less and less, limiting communication to the necessary. He stops wearing clothing, as it no longer fits his changing form. He becomes smaller and smaller, and when he is three feet tall, he begins to walk on all fours. At first this is awkward, but as time passes, his limbs even out, and soon he can't walk on two legs at all. His ears grow to points and creep up the side of his head. Grotesque alterations in his face make Grace shriek when she comes upon him unprepared.

Realizing she can't recall the last time she heard him speak, she says, "Roger?" He stares but doesn't respond. "Can you speak, Roger?"

He answers back a nearly silent meow.

Roger starts to avoid her, slinking around rooms and dashing under beds, then suddenly showering her with affection. He rubs his strange body against her legs.

One day, the doorbell rings and Grace answers it, believing Roger to be hidden away in another room. But as the deliveryman hands her a package, she feels a soft movement around her ankles. Her heart stops. Roger slinks in front of her, whisking his tail and sniffing at the man's boots. The man reaches down and pats Roger's head. "Now that," he says, "is a friendly cat. My girl-friend's cat looks just like him, but that thing—" He makes a quick movement with his hands, miming a cat that is dashing away.

When the door shuts, Grace picks Roger up by the midsection and stares into his face. He blinks. Holding him in front of her, she examines him all over, looking for some sign of the former Roger. He wriggles and claws her arm, drawing a small amount of blood. She sets him down, and he walks away, tail in the air and proudly swishing.

———

Spring comes again. Grace does all she can to make Roger happy, buying him jingling toys and catnip and a towering cat condo that overwhelms the living room. He seems content, but it's hard to tell. He spends most of his time on the windowsill, looking out with what could be satisfied fascination but that Grace worries might be tinged with longing. She considers looking among Roger's old things for the key to the rolltop desk. She could train herself to read his transformation book. There might be a way to change him back. But Grace doesn't try. To watch him go through another transformation—that would be too difficult, even if it would make him human again. It's easy to live with him, now he's a cat. She reminds herself that he's gotten what he wanted.

Much is going well in Grace's life: She's been promoted again at work, and she has started an amusing and flirtatious email correspondence with a college friend who recently moved to the city. One night, she meets this man for drinks, and then she takes him home with her. When they enter the apartment, Roger is sitting in front of the door, as if he has been waiting. "Oh," says the man, "is this your cat?" He reaches out a hand, but Roger springs away, disappearing somewhere behind the cat condo.

Grace sits on the sofa with the man. He kisses her. As his hands run over her body, Grace finds herself distracted, thinking about how Roger is hiding somewhere in the room. She stands and pulls the man into her bedroom, where they lie on the bed and quickly undress each other down to their underwear. Then he moves on top of her and kisses her cheeks, her neck, pulls down her bra straps, but Grace feels wrong and it's hard for her to breathe with him lying on top of her. She tries to shift out from under him, and though he readjusts, she still feels trapped until he sits up to remove her underwear. Once they're fucking, it's not so bad. Grace even feels a bit of pleasure.

In the morning, after the man leaves, Grace cries. She finds Roger in the living room. He rubs his body against her legs, then hops to her lap, and Grace stops crying. Her life is so much better than it used to be. She remembers a time before she knew Roger, when she had just moved to New York. She was in a small park standing next to a planter where people had discarded the stubs of their cigarettes. She had looked down into the planter and noticed that a few of these cigarettes were not fully smoked, not even half-smoked, and she had wondered who these people were, who cared so little about money that they discarded cigarettes after so little smoking. She had waited until no one was looking, reached into the planter, and taken one.

Yes, Grace thinks, she's better off now than at that distant moment. She doesn't even smoke anymore. Her job, the comfortable apartment—but none of that seems to matter. Her accordion remains locked away, she's not the person she'd wanted to be, and most of all, she can't stop missing Roger—Roger as he once was. A quote from her recent reading comes to mind, something about women loving longest after all hope is gone. But then, Grace tells herself, the writer was thinking of different circumstances; it's ridiculous to apply such an idea to her situation. Remembering again the cigarette planter, Grace decides she's happy. She must be. She strokes Roger's head, the softness of his fur. He stretches his paws out over her lap and purrs.

About the Author

HEATHER MONLEY'S fiction has appeared in *The Kenyon Review* (as the winner of the 2013 Short Fiction Contest), *Crazyhorse*, and McSweeney's *Internet Tendency*. She has an MFA from Columbia University and a BA from Dartmouth College, and she lives in Mountain View, California.

MINOR SAINTS

MARY-KIM ARNOLD

1.

I dreamed you
at my sink in your socks,
you were slicing an apple
then eating it

our mothers both gone now
idle ghosts
knocking at radiator pipes
at a register only dogs
can hear

2.

we tried for years

we walked the grove of trees
they say is haunted

built a temple of stones
with our hands

cradled the hot damp bodies
of dying animals to our chests
while all around us apples ripened
and fell

we prayed

we lit candles in the names
of saints we knew
and those we wished for:

Marguerite, saint of small
and common birds

Horatio, steeping tea

St. Ida reciting novenas
in the night weeping while
her children slept

3.

at the checkout, a woman coughs
into her open palm

her twin daughters behind her
laughing
their hair in braids

at night, I dream them
these cheerful braided daughters
linking arms and growing large
as they lumber through the streets

tall as mailboxes

then as lampposts

then as houses

I shout at them in greeting
to ask about their mother

but I don't think they can hear me
at this distance

About the Author

MARY-KIM ARNOLD'S short fiction has appeared in *Tin House* (online), *Wigleaf, Swarm Quarterly,* and the *Pinch.* Her poems have been published in *burntdistrict, Two Serious Ladies, Sundog Lit,* and elsewhere. She has also written for HTMLGIANT, *The Lit Pub,* and *The Rumpus,* where she is Essays Editor. She received her MFA in fiction from Brown University and is studying poetry at the Vermont College of Fine Arts. She plays bass in the band WORKING and lives in Rhode Island with her husband and children.

Forsyth Harmon © 2014

SANDWICHES FOR STEVE

SEAN ADAMS

The ground shakes so much in the morning that our supervisor, Dic, turns off the conveyer belt and calls a meeting. He tells us that in light of the recent seismic activity, we should take extra care to keep our feet planted. In fact, he escalates having our feet planted from being Always a Good Idea to a Strong Suggestion, which is serious, considering that a Strong Suggestion is just one step away from Official Policy.

Official Policy means there are forms to sign, and printing forms costs money, and the factory hates spending money, so they do just about anything to avoid making stuff Official Policy. But in this case, it turns out to be necessary because, around lunchtime, there's a full-blown earthquake, which opens up a giant chasm across the floor, tears the conveyer belt in half, and swallows up Steve. Had it been anyone else, maybe they could've just said, "Accidents happen," and moved on. Not Steve, though. Not when he had so openly mocked the Strong Suggestion to Keep Our Feet Planted by doing a crude song and dance in which he rhymed *feet* with *skeet*.

And when I hear that it was Steve who got swallowed up, all I can think is, *Close call!* Because even though I couldn't come up with any lyrics of my own and even though I couldn't really see the moves he was doing (it looked to be equal parts pelvic thrusting and tap dancing through the blur of the eyedrops), there was definitely a part of me that thought maybe I should join in just for the sake of doing something spontaneous, given how lacking my life has been in that department, especially since Tiffany left.

But I didn't dance and I didn't sing and Steve did. Now, Steve is somewhere deep in the chasm that's torn the factory in half, and I'm up here, back in the meeting room, sitting with everyone else while Dic and his secretary, Sandy, pass out forms on the new Official Feet-Planted Policy, and I wouldn't trade places with Steve for all the dancing in the world.

When everyone has a form, Dic says, "Feel free to take these home and read them later when you can actually make out the words." But none of us do. We all just sign them where we think the signature line is and leave the room. "Work for the rest of the day is canceled," Dic tells us as we file out, "on account of bad weather, or whatever the hell you call an earthquake."

Outside the meeting room, we hang around until one of the security guys makes us leave. Nobody likes going home early, since going home early means having to do the whole commute before the eyedrops wear off.

Here's the deal with the eyedrops: The factory makes a secret product. So secret that we, the people who put it together, aren't allowed to know what it is. Every morning, after the security guys search our lunch boxes for cameras, men in lab coats administer eyedrops that blur out all but the broad outlines of things. These eyedrops last just over eight hours and wear off all at once. Everything looks blurry one second, then you blink, and everything clears up. I call that blink, "the Essential Blink." It's great when it happens, but it makes for a lot of stressful blinks leading up to it. You can't help yourself from thinking, *Could this be it? Could this possibly be the Essential Blink?* And then when it's not, it makes you that much more anxious for the next blink.

I imagine this to be a universal feeling, but that's likely not the case. The rest of these people probably go through their days without ever worrying what the next blink will bring. They probably don't ever even wonder about what the factory makes. Me? I can't *stop* wondering about it.

I'm just so damn curious.

I spend every minute at the conveyer belt coming up with theories, and I spend every coffee break discussing these theories with Donald. Donald is one of the guys I share a coffee station with. The other guys are Francis and, formerly, Steve. They keep us to four per coffee station so that we can't organize.

———

The next morning, we get some exciting news, or at least it's exciting for me: the conveyer belt is still off-line, so we'll have to pass the parts along by hand. "Be sure to move as quickly as you can," Dic says. "That means no pausing, no chatting, and absolutely no feeling up the product." Then he says, "Webster, you want to stand up?" A giant blur of a man rises from his seat at the conference table. Webster, Dic explains, is a shot-putter. When the product gets to the chasm, Webster will shot-put it over. "Webster almost went to the Olympics," Dic tells us.

Someone raises a hand and asks, "How come 'almost'?"

Webster remains quiet for a moment, and then, in a voice as deep as the chasm itself, says, "There was this one time that I didn't throw it far enough."

And his voice turns out to be only half as alarming as the grunt he makes every time he shot-puts a product, which is just about every twenty seconds all day long, each grunt followed by a "Product secured," from whoever's catching on the other side. I don't let it bother me, though; instead I concentrate deeply and tune out all the noise around me so I can really focus on feeling up the product and drawing conclusions.

When it's handed to me, the product is just a Cylindrical Thing. I take a Rod Thing out of the box behind me, insert it into the top of the Cylindrical Thing, and turn it three times until it clicks into place. Today, I turn nice and slow with one hand so that the other gets a few extra seconds to grope around for something—a texture, a button, a hole, anything that might give some hint as to what I'm holding—but nothing presents itself.

"I didn't find anything," I tell Donald at our first break. Our coffee station sits right next to the chasm, and we keep peering over our backs to make sure it hasn't gained any ground. Not that we'd really be able to tell.

"Nothing for me either," says Donald. For a while, with the eyedrops, I thought Donald wore a beret every day, but over time I've come to realize he just has beret-shaped hair. "There was a solid five minutes where I convinced myself it was a birdfeeder, and I got really excited," he adds, "but then I thought about it more, and the truth is, birdfeeders vary so wildly in design that they lack any universal characteristics, so saying something feels like a birdfeeder is pretty much like saying it could be anything. And besides, why make a birdfeeder in secret?"

"Maybe it's for a secret kind of bird," I say. "Like a bird that the government made in a science experiment, to use during wartime instead of planes."

"Hmm," says Donald like he's considering the possibility, but we both know it's a stupid idea that doesn't warrant further discussion, so we use the rest of our coffee break doing our other favorite thing: telling jokes about Dic's dick.

When he first came on to replace our old supervisor—a tall, soft-spoken man who referred to himself simply as Number 8—Dic made a huge deal about his name. He told us that his full name is Ricard without an *h*, so he figured he had to lose a letter in the nickname version in order for there to be balance in the universe. It seemed reasonable enough at the time, but then one day during a break, Donald said, "Wait—isn't *Dic* without a *k* like a dick without the end part?" We laughed and laughed and laughed until it was time to go back to work, and ever since then we've come up with new jokes about Dic's dick every day.

"What did the critics say about the movie based on Dic's dick?" I ask Donald.

"I don't know. What?" he says.

"It was okay, but it ended kind of abruptly."

"That's good," says Donald, without laughing.

We hear the bathroom door swing open, followed by an abrasive clacking sound, like a horse walking on tin hooves. Donald and I turn to see the blurry outline of Francis coming our way.

"Why do your feet sound so loud?" I ask.

Francis sighs, like he can't believe I asked that, and says, "Umm, cleats? For the new Feet-Planted Policy, duh!"

Francis looks like he either has bags under his eyes and thick eyebrows or he wears horn-rimmed glasses. Most people would say it's probably the bags and eyebrows, because why would anyone bother with glasses if their vision is going to be blurry anyway? And sure, that makes sense, but sometimes I still have the urge to punch him square in the face and see if anything falls off just to be sure. I'll admit, I'm not a big fan of Francis. He takes things too seriously, and he never joins in on coming up with theories about the product, or jokes about Dic's dick. He just sighs and talks down to us like he's some sort of genius.

"Most people would be satisfied just standing more firmly than before," he says, pouring a cup of coffee, "but not me. I'm being double careful, so I don't end up down there like Steve."

"Did someone up there say *Steve*?" Steve says from somewhere far below us. My back tenses up, and I look at Donald. His blurry outline has gone rigid as well. Francis drops his mug, which shatters loudly on the cement floor, and runs clacking to go find Dic. All the noise draws attention from the other coffee stations, and by the time Dic shows up, he has to push through a crowd just to get to the edge of the chasm. He calls down to Steve and asks him if he can see any way to get up.

"No, I can't see anything," Steve says. His voice sounds strained, like he's yelling as loud as he can, but up here, we can only just barely hear him. "It's pretty much pitch-black down here."

"Okay," says Dic, and I can swear he says, "Good," under his breath, but I can't be sure.

———

In the meeting room, Sandy puts a box on the table and takes out what appear to be several bright shapes.

"I'm excited to tell you all about a new initiative we have here at the factory," she says. Nobody ever refers to the factory by its name, not even those who presumably know it. "It's called the Sandwiches for Steve program. As many of you have probably heard, one of our coworkers, Steve, was swallowed up by the chasm that runs through our facility. Well, just because he's lost to the world doesn't mean he's lost his appetite! That's why we're going to be assigning each worker a day of the week and a meal: breakfast, lunch, or dinner. On that day, it is your responsibility to prepare Steve a sandwich for that meal. At various times throughout the day we will throw these sandwiches into the chasm, along with a water bottle that the factory has been generous enough to pay for, using money out of the holiday party budget."

I think about asking why we have a holiday party budget if we never have a holiday party, but like always in these meetings, I stay quiet. Someone else asks if we have to always make sandwiches for Steve or if we can prepare something else.

"We say a sandwich because it's one of the most catchable meals there is, as long as you wrap it in tinfoil," Sandy explains. "It's harder to catch soup, for example, unless it's in a really good container, but even with that, it could still hit a rock or something and crack open, and then you're out a good container and Steve's out a meal and potentially covered in soup in a place that doesn't have any napkins."

"Some hot soup on his head would serve him right for dancing during an earthquake!" someone shouts, inspiring a rumble of agreement from others. Dic, seated next to Sandy, quiets everyone down.

"Easy, guys," he says. "Sandy, why don't you tell us what all this stuff is for."

Sandy explains that the shapes on the table are craft materials, in case we want to include any notes or handmade greeting cards with the inaugural sandwich. "Although," she adds, "that's more of a thought-that-counts sort of thing. Between your vision-impaired handwriting and the total darkness of the chasm, the likelihood of Steve being able to read anything you write is pretty slim."

———

A few people forget their sandwich on their assigned day, a few people throw theirs wrong by accident, and a few people throw soup into the chasm out of spite, but for the most part the Sandwiches for Steve program gets off to a great start. Me? I love it. Or it's not so much that I love the program as I love making food for other people, because it reminds me of when I used to come home and cook dinner for Tiffany.

Tiffany is the last girl I dated, and the only one I've been able to keep things going with for more than a few days since starting at the factory. Tiffany suffered from a fear of being looked at. She enjoyed company and conversation but panicked whenever someone turned a pair of eyes on her. She had an oversized poncho and a catcher's mask that was custom-fitted on the inside with a two-way mirror that provided some protection for when she went to parties. But the outfit was hot and uncomfortable and put people off. As a result, she spent most of her time at home, keeping herself from feeling alone by carrying on conversations with photographs and filling all her empty chairs with tennis rackets wearing sunglasses. She probably wouldn't have spoken to me at all had it not been for the eyedrops.

We met when I was riding the bus home at midday after being let out early due to the conveyer belt overheating. I took the seat next to her and asked if she wouldn't mind telling me when we were getting close to my stop on account of my vision being not the greatest. That was all it took. Something like electricity pulsed through her blurry outline, and she just started talking and talking and talking, not even stopping to take a breath until we were long past where I was supposed to get off. Later, she told me it was like a dream come true, being able to speak to a real person who couldn't see her. She said it was like being behind a privacy curtain.

89

When I lived with Tiffany, the Essential Blink felt even more essential than ever. If it came before I arrived home, that meant at least the quick glimpse of her I got would be in focus before she ran and hid. If it hadn't come yet, then she registered as little more than a large eye floater as she made her escape. These days are different. There's no one else at home, and I don't have all that much worthwhile stuff to actually look at, so the Essential Blink is pretty much just like any other blink, except it's easier to read labels afterward.

I'm thinking about this while making my sandwich at night—just one for me, since tomorrow's not my day to throw one to Steve—when I get a wild idea. What if the eyedrops don't last a set number of hours after all? What if they last a set number of blinks? And the Essential Blink isn't just the blink that happens when they wear off, it's what *makes* them wear off, like it's the final blink you need to fulfill the eyedrops' predetermined blink quota for the day? I consider saving this theory and pitching it to Donald at our first coffee break the next day, but then I decide, no. In the name of spontaneity and excitement, I will test it myself. I will burn through a day's worth of blinks before lunch.

As soon as I get onto the floor the next morning, I start blinking rapidly and keep it going for a half hour. Then I start to feel a bit woozy. The strobe effect on top of the blurry vision makes me light-headed, and I struggle to stay on my feet. My grip on the product is limp and clammy. A few times I stumble forward and bump my thigh hard on the broken conveyer belt. A bruise will form; I can feel it, but it doesn't deter me. On the contrary, I double down on my resolve and try to blink even quicker than before. That's when I feel something creeping up my throat. I quickly hand off the product that I'm holding and vomit behind my box of Rod Things.

"You okay?" asks Harris. Harris is the guy who hands me the Cylindrical Things. He either has a mustache or some sort of terrible upper lip infection.

"Yeah, I'm fine," I say, getting back in line. "Just one of those liquidy coughs."

"It sounded like a soda can exploding," Harris says, "but a little thicker, so maybe like a can of breakfast drink." I assure Harris that everything is okay, and we go back to work, but only for a few minutes before the whistle blows and we get an unscheduled coffee break. I go to the bathroom, swish some water around in my mouth. I consider locking the door and picking up where I left off with the blinking in there, but just the thought makes me shiver and gag, so I decide to give up on the experiment and head to my coffee station. On my way there, I pass Webster, still at his post, having a heated discussion with Dic.

"I don't care how your arm feels," Dic hisses. "We have to keep this stuff moving."

"I'm not built for this," Webster says. His voice is so deep that I feel it in my chest, even when he whispers. "I can't shot-put for eight hours, five days a week. When we were training for the Olympics, we had to shot-put seven, maybe ten things max, then we'd get a few days off for our arms to recover."

"Well, I guess it's a real shame you didn't qualify for the Olympics then, huh?" Dic replies coldly.

At the coffee station, Francis and Donald fill me in on what they've heard from the people around them in the line: Something's wrong with Webster. He's been going slow all morning, and the product's really piling up. This coffee break is so that he can get back on track.

"Yeah, I heard him talking to Dic about that," I say.

"Speaking of Dic," Donald says, and then he launches into a new joke about Dic's dick. Dic is in Uganda, and he's looking for a motel. He goes into one and asks if they have any rooms with king beds. The desk guy says no; they only have single beds. Also, the motel doesn't accept money. Dic will have to pay in candy wrappers or by poking himself with knitting needles.

Donald stops halfway through. "Oh, wait," he says. "Now that I think about it, the word I was going to use to describe Dic's dick doesn't mean what I thought it did, so it won't make any sense." Then he gets quiet and sullen.

It's not the first time Donald's had to abandon ship on a joke about Dic's dick due to a vocabulary issue, so I know the best thing to do is just leave him alone, which means either talking to Francis or not talking at all. So the three of us sip our coffee, not talking at all. I turn and watch Webster work, by which I mean I watch the Webster-sized cloud swirl at the edge of the chasm. It's true what Francis and Donald heard. Something seems wrong. His grunts sound more strained than usual, and a few times I hear a clank at the other side of the chasm before the guy calls, "Product secured"—like Webster threw it just a little short of his man.

And then there comes a heave that is way off. The swirl, the grunt—it's all just terrible. A few extra seconds later someone calls, "Product secured." But it's not the normal guy. It's Steve.

———

"So you can't see anything, right?" shouts Dic into the chasm.

"Nope," Steve calls back up. There isn't a crowd this time, because Dic wouldn't allow one, but with our coffee station's location, we hear it all.

"What about him holding it?" Sandy says, standing next to Dic. "He's going to have it in his hands a long time. If he's a creative-thinking type, he might start to draw conclusions."

"Are you much of a creative thinker, Steve?" Dic calls down.

"I don't know," Steve yells. "I never took any creativity tests."

"Well, that's a good sign," says Sandy. Dic says something in agreement, but he doesn't sound happy about any of this, which makes sense. A factory worker whose eyedrops are long worn off is at this moment holding a half-finished product he's not allowed to know about.

Just behind Dic and Sandy, Webster sits on the ground, suffering through flashbacks from the time he didn't make the Olympics. "I'm sorry, coach," he says to no one. "Give me one more shot, coach. I can clear it, I swear."

They give us another half day, but again, I don't leave until someone makes me. I just hang out by my coffee station, thinking of what it must be like to be Steve right now, holding the half-finished product, feeling it up all day long, finding its every nook and cranny. Suddenly, I don't feel so lucky for not dancing after all. Objectively speaking, being out of the chasm is better than being in it, but imagine the conclusions a creative thinker like me could draw in Steve's position. All that time with nothing to do but touch the product? Just fantasizing about it is enough to make me giddy for the rest of the day, and through the night too, and I'm still feeling it the next morning when they search our lunch boxes and give us our eyedrops but then usher us into the meeting room instead of onto the factory floor.

"We just wanted to bring everyone together to thank you for your participation in the Sandwiches for Steve program," says Sandy. "The people from the corporate office even gave us a little letter." She holds up what looks like a nondescript white square. "It says, 'On behalf of the entire company, we issue this formal and official thanks for providing sandwiches to a coworker in need. Because of your generosity, said coworker did not starve to death, which is something you should all feel the utmost pride in. As the Sandwiches for Steve program is now coming to its conclusion, you may once again resume packing only as much food as you require and no more. Thank you. Sincerely, The Corporate Office.' Isn't that such a nice letter? And it's printed on some very nice paper too. Here, I'll pass it around."

Everyone mumbles that Sandy's right, the paper does feel nice, but I don't mumble along, not even when it gets all the way down the table to me. Something seems wrong here. "Why are we concluding Sandwiches for Steve?" I ask without raising my hand.

Sandy starts to answer with something about confidential information, but Dic cuts her off. "It's pretty simple, actually," he says. "As of last night, Steve no longer works for us. I was looking through our files, and it appears he was too busy fooling around somewhere between here and the middle of the earth to sign the form acknowledging that he read and understood the Official Feet-Planted Policy, and as I'm sure you're all well aware, refusal to comply with new policies is an offense that can result in termination."

"But he still has to eat," I say. A few faces turn toward me. I can't tell if they're giving me nasty looks or not. I keep talking. "He's stuck down there in the chasm. He can't make sandwiches himself."

"I'm glad you said that," Dic says, "because it reminds me that I've got some exciting news. The chasm is going away! I talked to the construction people this morning and hammered out the final details. They're coming in this weekend to fill the whole thing in. And once we've got that squared away, we'll get the conveyer belt up and running again."

Everyone mumbles approvingly, except me again. "What about Steve?" I ask. "Are you going to fill it in with him in it?"

"What Steve does from here on out is really up to him," Dic says. "Honestly, he's lucky that we haven't called the police for trespassing."

I have more concerns, but something about the sternness of Dic's voice tells me it's time to shut up, so I do.

Someone else asks how we're going to get the product over the chasm for the time being. Dic says that Webster, who has recovered both physically and emotionally from yesterday's incident, will continue in his role. But to keep him from burning out again, he'll throw only every other product. Those that he doesn't throw, Dic tells us, will be launched across the chasm using a modified T-shirt cannon that should be delivered sometime before lunch.

———

For the rest of the day, I'm quiet. I don't even talk about the product or make jokes about Dic's dick during my coffee breaks. I just think about Steve and feel bad, and then I think about the last time I felt this bad, which was the day I woke up and Tiffany wasn't there anymore.

When she agreed to move in with me, part of the deal was that I had to put some money toward a sewing machine and a few rolls of fabric. She didn't tell me what she wanted it for, but the first day I came home after buying it, I saw that she'd made a curtain. I thought that was nice, considering the curtains I had were ratty and stained. By the next day she'd made another, and another the day after that too, and another and another and another, until the curtains outnumbered the windows by five to one. But they weren't for the windows. Tiffany hung them from the ceiling, turning the apartment into a maze, so she'd have more places to hide. "Now, we can be in the same room together without all the attempts at eye contact," she told me. "I did this for us."

It sounded sweet when she said it, but the truth was I hated those curtains. It became a chore to get from one end of the apartment to another. I wiped my hands on my pants constantly, because I could never find the sink, and once, late at night, after trying and failing to locate the toilet for nearly a half hour, I urinated into a spare garbage bag, tied it up, and hid it on the fire escape until the next morning. Still, I never said a bad word about those curtains. I never cut any holes or tore any down. I considered them to be like the coffee at work: not great, but good enough to keep things going.

Except, things didn't keep going. I woke up one morning and found nothing but a note on Tiffany's side of the bed. She wrote that she had begun to feel my eyes through the fabric. She said it made sense, that given all the time they spent underutilized during the day, my eyes probably had all sorts of energy stored up to see through things other eyes couldn't. "So I need to go now," she wrote, "but thanks for being so understanding."

I think about Tiffany, and I think about Steve, and I think about how going along with things seems easy on paper, but then there are all these hidden emotional fees, and after a while they really add up and you end up feeling crummier than if you'd just put your foot down and said, "No! I will not feel lost in my own living room!" or "No! I'm not just going to forget about the guy in the chasm!"

At night, when I'm getting tomorrow's lunch ready, I take out two slices of bread. Then, without giving myself time to think about it, I take out two more.

———

"I believe you were told not to pack extra food anymore," says the security guy the next morning. He has in his hands my two foil-wrapped sandwiches.

"Oh, I forgot about that," I say. The security guy sighs and goes to throw one of the sandwiches away, but I tell him no, that he shouldn't do that. I should take it and force myself to eat both at lunch so that the uncomfortable fullness that follows will serve as a bitter lesson as to why I need to remember stuff better. The security guy considers this for a moment, then nods. He even pats me on the back and commends my discipline. After that, a guy in a lab coat gives me my eyedrops and I head out onto the factory floor.

All morning, I can barely concentrate. My hand is shaky on the Rod Things. I slip while turning one, and it rubs my palm raw, but I bite my lip and act like nothing happened so that Harris doesn't get worried.

At our first break, I don't drink any coffee. I already feel jittery enough without it. Donald notices and asks, "Do you know something about the coffee that I don't know?"

"No," I say. Then I add, "Nothing about the coffee."

Donald starts to ask me what I'm talking about, but Francis comes clacking up, still wearing his cleats like an idiot, so I don't get a chance to explain. Instead, I tell a joke about Dic's dick.

"Why was there a picture of Dic's dick in the math book?" I ask.

"I don't know. Why?" says Donald.

"Because they saw that it didn't have an ending and thought it must be pi, the number that goes on forever," I say.

"Intellectual humor. I like that," Donald says, without laughing.

"Thanks," I say. "I thought of it last night while I was making my lunches."

When noon comes around, I go to the chasm as casually as I can, call down to Steve, and throw him his sandwich. A few people hear me and come over to ask if I missed the part yesterday about the Sandwiches for Steve program ending. I don't say anything, but there must be something about my blurry outline that implies something is about to happen, because they don't leave; they just stand there looking down into the dark blur of the chasm like I do, and then even more people start to gather.

I'll admit that this sudden audience lends the situation even more spontaneity and excitement than I'd planned for, but I can barely feel it because I'm already at my limits in terms of both those categories. Here's the truth: The sandwich I've thrown Steve isn't a sandwich. It's a tiny flashlight between two pieces of bread.

"Don't bite down too hard on that one, Steve," I call into the chasm.

What I hope will happen next is that Steve will remove the flashlight, turn it on, and see what the half-formed product is. He'll call it up to us, we'll all hear, which will probably mean we'll all be fired, but especially me. The chasm will be filled with Steve in it, or maybe it won't. Maybe they'll just leave it there, because with the secret out, the factory might have to shut down and maybe the whole company too. Dozens, maybe even hundreds of people could lose their jobs over this, but I don't care.

I'm just so damn curious.

About the Author

SEAN ADAMS has published work in *Hobart*, *Hayden's Ferry Review*, *Mid-American Review*, and McSweeney's *Internet Tendency*. His story "The Astronaut Who Forgot" was a finalist for the *Missouri Review*'s 2013 Jeffrey E. Smith Editors' Prize in Fiction. He is a graduate of Bennington College and currently lives in Seattle.

out south

NATE MARSHALL

No more to build on there. And they, since they
Were not the one dead, turned to their affairs.

—ROBERT FROST, "OUT, OUT"

In Chicago kids are beaten. They crack
open: they pavement. They don't fight, they die.
Bodies bruised blue with wood. Cameras catch
us killing, capture danger to broadcast

on Broadways. We Roseland stars, made players
for the press. Apes caged from first grade until.
Shake us. We make terrible tambourines.
Packed into class, kids passed like kidney stones.

Each street day is unanswered prayer for peace,
News gushes from Mom's mouth like schoolboy blood.
Ragtown crime don't stop, only waves—hello.
Crime waves break no surface on news—goodbye.

Each kid that's killed, one less mouth to free lunch,
a fiscal coup. Welcome to where we from.

About the Author

NATE MARSHALL is from the South Side of Chicago. He currently serves as a Zell Postgraduate Fellow at the University of Michigan, where he received his MFA. He is a member of the poetry collective Dark Noise. A Cave Canem Fellow, his work has appeared in *Poetry* magazine, *Indiana Review*, the *New Republic*, *[PANK]* Online, and in many other publications. He was the star of the award-winning full-length documentary *Louder Than A Bomb* and has been featured on HBO's *Brave New Voices*. He is an assistant poetry editor for *Muzzle*. Nate is the founder of the Lost Count Scholarship Fund that promotes youth violence prevention in Chicago. Nate won the 2014 Hurston/Wright Amistad Award and the 2013 Gwendolyn Brooks Open Mic Award. He is also a rapper.

Maryanna Hoggatt © 2013

Michael Hirshon © 2013

HIGHWAY WITH GREEN APPLES

BY BAE SUAH

Translated by Sora Kim-Russell

We take a drive one day down a secluded highway through the countryside. As he's sitting behind the wheel, I ask him, "Did you see a cat pass in front of the car just now?"

"Of course."

He responds nonchalantly while fumbling with one hand for a cigarette. The late-autumn sky is heavy with clouds and looks as if it has been draped in dark and light curtains. A line of larch trees stretches all the way down to the end of the gray highway. The road ends at a rundown street that leads to a small, unfamiliar town, where women selling green apples will be sitting along the side of the street.

I am one week away from my twenty-fifth birthday. I hate being that age. That age is neither as fresh and full of life as fifteen years nor as jaded as the afternoon of thirty-five years. I never know what the next day will bring, so I am always uneasy.

"They say it's bad luck when a cat crosses your path," I tell him.

"Do they?"

"They say something bad will happen. Especially if it's a black cat, like that one."

"Black cat?"

He takes his hands off the steering wheel for a moment and considers this. The road is quiet and monotonous. All there is to see on either side are low, unchanging hills and fields planted with corn and pumpkin. With a week left to go before turning twenty-five, I tell myself that there must be a river nearby. Longing for that blue-green water, I lean out the car window into the wind.

"That cat wasn't black," he says. "You saw it wrong. It was gray with black spots. I'm sure of it."

I think, *It was black, I know it was.* But then I think, *Who cares? What difference does it make?* And I keep my mouth shut. Outside, where the tall grass lies flat in the wind, there are no people—only road, and more road. I will never forget just how beautiful the late autumn is.

"Want an apple?" he asks.

When I don't respond, he points to the paper bag of green apples, the ones we have just bought on the side of the road in the small, dust-covered town. Ah, right, we have apples. Green apples.

The woman who came to the car to sell us the apples was wearing a thickly woven scarf. He had pulled over near the highway and was busy studying the map. He made it sound spontaneous, but he'd had a destination in mind. A fishing village on the west coast—not too small but not so big that you would notice it right away. He tells me it's a tourist resort during the summer, but by that time of the year, it will practically be in hibernation.

"How do you know about this place?" I ask him. "I've never heard of it."

I had stared at the woman's chapped, reddened cheeks and wound up buying apples from her. They came in a paper bag that crinkled and gave off an old, musty smell. There must have been an orchard nearby. Her faded, hand-knit scarf covered half of her face. The piano music playing at full volume inside the car echoes far down the deserted road. Was it Rachmaninov? Tchaikovsky? Maybe a Schubert arpeggio? He keeps so many tapes in the car that I never know what we are listening to. The music reaches a shrill, intense part that contrasts with the surreal calm of the street. Then it subsides and turns dark as death, and the pianist lets out a deep breath. The tall larch trees that line the highway stand against the backdrop of the gray evening sky like an old watercolor. Women selling green apples on a dusty road. He had pulled the cash from his wallet without taking his eyes off the map. A dark-blue bus swept past the car with a dull clatter. Nearly invisible dust settled onto the woman's eyes and dry lips. The buildings are short, and the signs are old and flaking. The inside of one building, where the door stands open, is dark and low-ceilinged. A dry late-autumn breeze carries the scent of boiled beans and dried fish. I want to get out of the car and walk slowly down the street. Yes, it would be nice to live here and sell green apples in paper bags. I see myself from behind, walking back to a home next to a river out past the low hills, dragging my heavy feet as the night grows dark. On that autumn day of my twenty-fifth year, I have a lump in my throat.

"I went there once a long time ago," he says. "I think one of my high school friends was living there at the time. You can go fishing, and they have summer rentals. I don't know if he still lives there. But we used to be close."

I gaze at the side of his face and bite into an apple. I am a twenty-five year-old who goes to bed every night wondering what I will do the next day. By now, all the other women I know who went to the same all-girls high school as me are at their most self-assured, having married or living as career women in the big city, but I am as unsure of myself as I was at fifteen. He starts the car. Fallen leaves swirl up as if in a typhoon. He says, "From here we head straight west," and adds, "the last stretch is unpaved." He keeps checking the map. We get lost along the way, so it's pitch-black by the time we reach our destination. A dog won't stop barking, and the waves are loud. His high school friend is still living there.

"Long time no see," the friend tells him. "We don't get many visitors this time of year. The fishing isn't that good here. Truth is, I've been thinking more and more about leaving this place."

His friend says he wants to move back to the big city to get a job and enjoy the unsentimental nature of organized society for a change. The three of us walk along the beach in the dark, the sand coarse and the waves high. Beer and Coca-Cola cans and disposable chopsticks lie scattered among the rocks; lights from fishing boats sparkle on the dark sea. We occasionally stop to sit on the rocks, where they smoke cigarettes and talk about the old days. I sit quietly, as I don't know any of the people they are talking about, including the many women whose names come up. When the waves dampen our shoes, we get up and walk back the way we came. I trail soberly after them, unable to keep up with the conversation. His friend occasionally turns to say, "Watch your step," as if he has just remembered that I am there. Dawn approaches.

After the trip, I do not see him again for two years. I never learn whether his old high school friend left the village to return to the big city. We arrive in the dead of night and leave at dawn when the fog is thick, so all I remember are sounds—the barking dog, the crashing waves. He sips coffee while driving carefully through the early morning fog. The air is filled with the scent of the invisible sea.

"Feels like we're floating in a dream," I say.

I dip my palms into the damp fog. He keeps humming along to the song coming from the tape deck and doesn't say anything.

You don't know, do you? How much I love you.
My love for you will never change,
even after an ocean of time has passed.

How long is an ocean of time? Feelings as countless as grains of sand. Distances as far-flung as the sky. How much is that, I wonder. The song keeps playing.

No matter how far you go,
like the wind, I'll be with you.

I take a bite out of the last of the green apples rolling around in the backseat. The sour, astringent taste fills me like fog. I look over at the side of his face and think, *Even if we break up, you won't be forgotten.*

Later, over the phone, he tells me, "I met someone. I think I'm in love. She's tiny and cute. You would like her. I told her all about you. She's . . ."

Here, he lights a cigarette. I hear the all-too-familiar sound of his lighter over the phone. The blue-green flame.

"She really puts me at ease. It's different than when I'm with you. Oh, don't get me wrong. I'm not saying I had a problem with you. Not at all. It's just that, with her, I never feel anxious about what I'm supposed to do next. I could never cheat on someone like her."

He exhales a long puff of smoke. I can picture the blue cloud spreading thinly through a darkened room. I hear the sound of dinner being made downstairs in the house where I am renting a spare room. A cat meows, and the scent of roasting fish is in the air. A week has passed since we ate green apples together in a village on the west coast. It is the evening of my twenty-fifth birthday.

"I wish you were a different type of girl," he continues. "The type who cries and refuses to let go when a guy breaks up with her. The type who says, 'How dare you see another woman, I won't stand for it.' If you were that type, you would never have gotten this call from me. But, we were good in the beginning! You said so yourself."

Those words—*You said so yourself*—sound so oddly like begging that I find myself saying yes despite myself. He forgot it was my birthday. I don't feel like reminding him, either. And that is how I end up turning twenty-five. During the two years that we dated, he gave me a gift to celebrate every occasion—my birthday, the anniversary of the day he bought a dress shirt from me at the department store where I worked, the anniversary of our first date. If I told him it's my birthday, he would buy me a gaudy printed scarf or an African-style necklace. That's the kind of girl he likes.

"Remember our first date?" he asks. "I was so nervous I couldn't sleep the night before. We saw a movie together. It was a French movie, and I thought about trying to kiss you in the dark."

It wasn't a French movie but a 1960s' Italian film that was playing at a small revival house. And I had left for our date thinking that I wouldn't mind having sex with him that night. It was late by the time the film ended, and we missed the last subway train while drinking cold beer at a pub afterward. We held hands and walked for hours in the dark past shuttered shops along city streets littered with black plastic garbage bags. Old newspapers fluttered in the wind. What did I wear that night? A blue dress with a white sash. Black high heels to make my legs look longer. Clear polish on my nails. When I let down my hair, which I'd tied into a high ponytail, at a corner of a darkened building, he thought I was trying to seduce him.

"You don't have to do this," I say. "I wish you wouldn't worry about me. I'm not that upset about it."

I think back to elementary school. My handwriting was always neat and perfect, and during class, I kept my eyes on the swaying hem of my teacher's dress. She would hand back my pristine homework that never had any eraser marks on it and praise me by patting me on the head with a hand that smelled like soap. "You're such a good girl," she would say. "Keep it up."

"You told me from the start," he says. "That you were only seeing me because you were depressed. That we would break up eventually. Once I met a girl I really liked."

"Yes, I did."

"You said you would turn into a good girl, a virtuous one, and leave me for good."

"Yeah, so don't worry about me," I tell him. "You have nothing to worry about. I'm not going to run off and become a nun or start drinking or anything."

The house fills with the scent of *dwenjang* soup, which the landlady always serves at dinnertime. The landlord's chickens cluck in the back garden, and the rose vines growing on the gray outer wall where the paint is peeling away sway in the November breeze. Salarymen returning home to their families pause to buy cardboard boxes of grapes at the store and to smoke outside the subway station, which is surrounded by buildings that rent out small studio apartments. It's a typical evening, unchanged and seemingly never to change. When I first found this house, my friend So-yeong said, "I don't like it. It's everything I can't stand."

"So?" I said. "You're not the one who's going to live here. And it's what I can afford."

"What I can't stand is the petit bourgeois air that fills these places. I get this ominous feeling that hiding somewhere in these alleys is a neighborhood bully who never quite grew up. Do you want to live like a character in that TV show, *Three Families Under One Roof*, crammed into a tiny spare room next to all these poor families?"

I hate those things, too. Until recently, I was living with So-yeong in her apartment, which was old, dark, and dirty, like an abandoned ship on the verge of sinking. The fire escape with its rusted, broken railing was barely hanging on, and the building housed a poker den where salarymen who worked in a nearby office park would gather, their eyes bloodshot and ties loosened, and a piano school on the second floor where primary school students carrying little keyboards in their bags would show up like a relentless swarm of bugs once the deathly silence of midday had passed. The monotonous Czerny étude that would start to drone in the early evenings was probably overheard by a typist in the bathroom of a small office nearby, where she was touching up her lipstick and anxiously checking the clock. With the dark sunset reflecting in the bathroom mirror, she would turn and check how she looked from the back and then gather up her makeup and run back to her seat. She would still have fifteen minutes left to go before she could leave for the day.

I keep going.

"Do you remember those green apples, from the last time we took a trip?"

Why am I suddenly thinking about those green apples?

"Green apples? Oh, those horrible sour apples. They made my mouth pucker."

"I remember the women who were selling those apples. It was a shabby little street. The women were covered in dust and just watching the cars race down the highway. And they were all bundled up in thick scarves."

"What's wrong with you? You're always trying to shut me up by saying something ridiculous. Why can't you take anything seriously?"

"You know what I thought about back then? I thought about going back to that street someday and becoming one of those women who sell green apples."

"Instead of selling shirts in a department store?"

He sounds a little hurt.

"I don't know why I thought that either. I just got this premonition that someday I would be old and poor like those women and wind up selling apples on a dusty highway. And terrible green apples at that. I would stand there until evening, until I was sure that no one was coming to buy my apples. Until it was completely dark, my face covered in a thick, hand-knit scarf, staring down a road that leads to some far-off place I'll never reach."

Because life has not turned out the way I wanted it to. Because that's how it always is—as a child, you get no love from your parents, and at school, you get bad grades and never catch anyone's eye. And after you're all grown up, you keep peeking in the door of the gynecology clinic, and then wait for an hour, and another hour, at the café where a man has promised to meet you, gulping down several cups of weak coffee before leaving alone in the dark. Then, to top it off, the cat that crosses your path one day on a highway with green apples turns out to be a black cat.

———

The following afternoon, I bump into one of my cousins. She is eagerly picking out a necktie when she spots me and comes over to say hello.

"I didn't know you work here," she says.

"I didn't tell anyone at home."

"Want to get some coffee?"

She looks like she has a lot to tell me. I dread, and hate, this. *Home, family, dropping out of college, runaway daughter*—the words waver before my eyes. Everyone always wants to know why. They bring it up lightly, the way you would ask a child why she didn't do her homework, then they light a cigarette, pull the ashtray closer, lean way back in the chair, stretch their legs out, and wait for me to answer. I hate it.

"Do you have something to ask me?" I say.

"No, I won't ask any questions. I just wanted to know if you want to get coffee with me."

True to her word, we go for coffee. She tells me that since I left home, she's married the medical student she was dating. Come to think of it, there is something about her that suggests a housewife.

"Did you get married?" She raises her coffee cup to her lips.

"No."

She slowly lowers the cup.

"How've you been getting by?" she asks.

"I'm managing okay. But don't ask me where I'm living, and don't tell me to call my parents."

"I thought you got married. I thought you ran away to be with a man your parents didn't approve of. That's what we all imagined. I heard you wrote it in a letter. This is a surprise."

I feel sorry to have disappointed them. I can't tell her that I ran away simply because I felt like it.

"Eun-gyeong told me she saw you in a car with a guy."

Eun-gyeong is my younger sister by two years.

"She said he was wearing a denim jacket and sunglasses. You were sitting quietly next to him with a flower pinned to your dress. She said you two drove right by her, but you didn't see her. I'm the only one she told. She was upset and said, 'Why doesn't she call home if she's happily married now?'"

"He's just a friend. I don't even see him anymore. Hey, you said you wouldn't ask any questions."

"Sorry." She sets the cup down hard.

"Are you going to tell them I work here?"

"Not if you don't want me to."

This cousin, the daughter of my mother's older sister, is the same age as me. We were close as children, and we even went to the same college. So we have been closer than friends. Now that she's married to a doctor and well-off, she must pity me.

"After you left home, you got an offer of marriage. You remember that brick house with the triangular roof, in the next neighborhood over? The matchmaker said that family's son thought you were pretty and wanted to marry you. Your mom had to lie and say you'd moved to the provinces for work. She said you weren't ready to get married yet."

I remember the guy. I used to run into him all the time at the bus stop on the way to school. He wasn't particularly memorable. He was always pretending to read things like *Newsweek*. I was the kind of girl who felt defeated at the sight of pretty girls walking around confidently. I never trust anyone who tells me I'm pretty or says they like me. It's the same insecurity I feel as when a teacher calls me by the wrong name on the first day of school. The night before I left home, I dropped bits of fish on the dinner table and broke a glass while washing the dishes. It was toward the end of summer vacation, and my report card had come to the house that day. Everyone was sweating, even with the fan turned on. My report card had one A and one D, and all the rest were Cs. The D was in statistics. My little sister Eun-gyeong was hiking in the mountains with her friends, and my older brother was irritated with everyone and everything because his girlfriend had just broken up with him. I hated statistics and hated my brother and hated my parents, who were watching TV with glum faces. Vacation would be over in a week, and classes would start again. Pretty girls of every shape and shade would fill the hallways and classrooms. I had finished washing the dishes and was in the yard clipping my fingernails. The sound of the nail clippers must have annoyed my brother because he stuck his head out the door and yelled at me to be quiet. My mother, who felt nothing for my father, discovered the glass I'd broken while doing the dishes and scolded me from inside the kitchen, as if she'd finally found the proper outlet for her frustration. Crickets chirped in the corner of the yard. I asked myself over and over, *When will I ever get out of here?* I had no hope of becoming a female doctor or simultaneous interpreter or even a modest office girl. I had always respected those women and looked up to them, as if they lived in a country that was off-limits to me. And I didn't want to live like my older married cousin—marrying a man like my father or brother, eating the kimchi my mother made, pumping out babies nonstop. If I'd been cute, smart, or charming like Eun-gyeong, maybe people would've liked me more. I thought about the job application I had turned in a few weeks earlier for the sales position at the department store. My brother yelled from the other room for me to bring him coffee. I sat down at my desk and wrote this note to Eun-gyeong:

Dear Eun-gyeong,

I am leaving. I have fallen in love, and I don't want to live at home anymore.

I paused for a moment and stared blankly at the words *fallen in love*. It wasn't true. I wasn't in love with anyone. That in and of itself made me sad. But I knew that Eun-gyeong would wonder why I left. The mere thought of loving someone who wasn't one of my family members made me so happy, I felt like I could fly. My brother kept shouting for coffee, and my mother kept yelling at me. I went to the kitchen to boil water. In my memory of these events, everything is foggy and gray, like an old black-and-white movie. I dragged my feet over to the stove to put the kettle on and then moved even more slowly to get a coffee cup. My brother opened the door and yelled.

"Who do you think you are? Is it too much to ask for a cup of coffee?

You're a woman, aren't you? What do you think you'll do once you're married? I shouldn't have to call for you all day long just to get a glass of water! You're pretty stuck-up for someone with grades like yours."

My father said to my mother, "What's wrong with her? She used to be a good girl. It's your fault she turned out that way. All she does is sulk."

My mother's face turned deathly pale. I witnessed all of this through the wide-open door of my parents' room.

"She takes after her aunt," my mother said. "You know as well as I do how stubborn and empty-headed that younger sister of yours is. Besides, it's not like I had her alone. Why do you blame everything on me?"

It seemed I would never meet a man who would be sweet to me, a man who would hold my hand as we crossed a raging river, a man who would come to mind whenever I got sick. That's what I thought about as I tipped the hot kettle over the coffee cup. If I ever did meet a man like that, I would think of him as the person in my note, the one I'd "fallen in love" with. On that night, before running away from home, I felt certain that just because practically every single person found someone to marry did not mean that they'd found a love as gentle as a spring breeze or that shook them up like a midsummer storm. I was certain of this. I also suspected that I stood among the have-nots in that respect. *Brother,* I thought, *you may be able to strut around in front of us and take the last chicken leg for yourself and never once wash your own socks, but no matter how loudly you yell, you cannot stop me from leaving.* I leaned against the rusted kitchen door and listened to my brother slurp his hot coffee for the last time.

In the department store café, my cousin seems determined to not let me go. She doesn't seem to care that I am working and that, unlike her, I need this job to get by.

"Eun-gyeong is finishing college this year. She's been taking design classes after school, too. She's so clever. Your mother loves to brag that it didn't cost her anything to send her to school. My brother Seop has been arguing with our mom about marriage. Right now they're at a stalemate."

She twirls her coffee spoon between her pale fingers. In the afternoons, the café gets as crowded as a subway train on a rainy evening at rush hour. The clattering of china is constant, and the air is thick with noise and the languid smell of coffee like nausea. People keep stomping back and forth on the hardwood floor of the café, and I am anxious because Yuseon, who just started work the day before, is watching the shop alone.

"Everything's different now that everyone's grown up. In the old days, all the cousins would get together every holiday to take a family portrait. Remember that shabby old photo studio on the edge of town? We used to huff and puff our way up three flights of stairs and stand in front of a dusty black velvet curtain, trying to catch our breath. Back when Grandma and Grandpa were alive."

"I have to get back to work. I can't stay here all day with you. Come visit me again sometime. Just don't tell anyone else. If you do, I won't talk to you anymore."

My voice is firm. She pays for the coffee and follows me out of the café, looking hurt.

"You're shopping for a necktie, right?" I ask. "I'll help you pick one out."

I want to be a little nicer to her. Also, I wonder if I'm too harsh, considering that we haven't seen each other in so long.

"No, it's fine," she says. "I was just window-shopping. I wasn't planning to buy anything. Sometimes when I'm bored, I come here to look around."

I remember which photo studio she was talking about. Both of our families used to go there to have portraits taken. One summer, we all got together for a family portrait. I wore a new white, polka-dotted dress. I think I was in high school at the time. My cousin was very pretty with bright red cheeks and dewy lips. It might have been her brother Seop's birthday. My aunt wanted a picture of all six cousins together. That was probably the last time we had our pictures taken at that studio. We stood in front of the camera—my sister Eun-gyeong, my brother, Seop, and another cousin who were both in college at the time, my older female cousin who was married, and me. Back then,

I was fond of Seop because he was so different from my own brother, who was delicate, high-strung, and acted like a little prince when it came to food. Not that it made any difference now. A cousin isn't something solid. Neither is family. We held hands and sat in a semicircle. From behind the camera, which was covered with a black cloth, the photographer set off something that flashed like a firecracker. I was sweating. It was an extremely hot day, and all the windows in the photo studio were shut tight, making it hard to breathe from the heat of the flash and the smell of old dust. We were each promised a copy of the photo. The hem of my sweat-soaked dress fluttered as I ran down the dangerously steep and narrow wooden steps of the photo studio. Behind me, my cousin shouted for me to wait and go with her to get popsicles. From the staircase of the dark photo studio, the white dust-covered street in the midsummer sun dazzled my eyes. I could just make out some elderly women walking slowly beneath light-colored parasols. We ran across the street to the store that sold ice cream and bought strawberry popsicles. The rest of the family slowly emerged at last from the photo studio, wiping their sweat with handkerchiefs. Seop saw us and waved. A dust-covered taxi whooshed past down the center of the street. The breeze from the passing car whipped up my hair and the hem of my skirt, and one of the old women who was standing under a parasol and waiting for the bus looked me over. In that moment, I was dazzling, too. I sat on the curb and leaned back against a white railing and looked at the woman. I closed my eyes. The bus arrived, and people got on the bus. The road emptied again to white. A premonition came over me—a vague sadness, as if this exact feeling, this same summer day, would come around again sometime. As punishment for sitting in the dirt in my brand-new tailor-made white dress, I wound up having to scrub that dress clean by hand.

He liked to remind me of our first phone call. It was before we'd started seeing each other. He'd met me only once, but he wanted to see me again so badly that he went outside every night to the phone booth in front of his family's apartment at two in the morning and paced back and forth, drinking a can of beer. After several days of agonizing, he finally got up the courage to call and was surprised and a little disappointed when I wasn't put off by it but instead answered the phone as if he were a male cousin calling. I wished I had a story like that of my own. But it was different for me. That autumn afternoon, when we returned to the city from our long drive, the sky was so clear and pure blue that I erased all memory of the bitter aftertaste of those green apples. Everyone I saw looked beautiful, and because it was early afternoon on the last day of a long holiday weekend, the bright expanse of sycamore and cherry trees lining the road was like a painting that you wanted to keep looking at for no reason. I took out my sketchbook and started drawing.

"It doesn't make you carsick?" he asked.

"It's just a sketch," I said. "And anyway, it's not me drawing but a stranger inside of me who compels me to draw. When that happens, I have no choice but to draw, even while driving."

"Why do you talk like that?" He was always criticizing me for not sounding more like his mother or older sister. "Why can't you just say, 'I feel like drawing, so I have to draw.' I think you like it when I can't understand you."

I closed the sketchbook with a snap. He hated it when I did that. I did it on purpose. What happened to the docile, slightly sexy, five-foot-four shopgirl he thought he'd met? Me, the girl who never mended the buttons on his dress shirts or pierced her ears so that she could wear the same hoop earrings all the other girls wore, who spent her days off shut inside a cramped room all afternoon with unwashed hair, standing in front of an easel, drawing apples on a tray.

"It's not like you're a real painter," he said quietly. "And those apples are too green. They should be light green with hints of reddish-pink. When you draw them that way, they look creepy."

He once admitted that he'd felt disappointed to discover that I didn't know how to make pickled radishes or grilled fish, and wouldn't sweetly knot his neckties for him like I did when I was working. I'd told him I wasn't looking for a man who would be my rock in life. That was another shock to him.

"If you like painting that much, shouldn't you be a painter instead of working in a department store? If you don't want to live an ordinary life, then why are you dating a good-for-nothing like me, instead of finishing college and meeting someone in the same league as you?"

He steered the car toward an empty office park; the cold, bright sunlight was blinding. I didn't respond. A girl in her late teens looked our way, the crisp sound of her shoes ringing as she walked quickly along the border between the shadow of the buildings and the bright sunlight. Her cheeks, pale with makeup, were beautiful. Fallen leaves that hadn't yet lost their color skittered around the hem of her skirt.

The girl's black hair swayed around her pale cheeks. She disappeared into the shadow between two buildings, covering her face with the book she carried in her hand as if to ward off the wind. The street was empty again. People had not yet returned from their road trips to the coast or the mountains of Gangwon province, where the leaves were still frantically changing color.

"Do you want to go home?" he asked.

His voice was glum. I caught a faint whiff of his cologne as he turned his head to let his bangs spill over his forehead. I got out at the nearest subway station. We both looked sullen, as if angry for no particular reason. I irritably yanked my sketchbook out of the car and shoved the pencils into my bag any which way. Then I slowly counted to ten before looking back. The bright, empty street was cool and dazzled my eyes like a glass of foamy beer.

———

"Even though I've never been the type to cling to a guy, I can't stop thinking about him after I get home from one of our dates. And then I sit around waiting for him to call."

When we were in college, my cousin, who lived in the neighborhood, used to come over to our house for dinner and whisper things like this to me in my room. She wore makeup and imported brand-name sweaters. The same age as me, she was the kind of coed the guys wanted to date; she was spending more and more time in front of the mirror with each passing day. The TV was turned up loud in my parents' room, and my brother wasn't home yet. Eun-gyeong was changing clothes, saying she had to eat and run to her art lessons. My cousin chatted nonstop about the medical student she had started dating. She said he was on the honor roll, was over five foot nine and handsome, and had a deep, intimate voice. I got into bed next to her, crawled under the blanket, and thought about a guy I'd never met. On her way out of the house, Eun-gyeong grabbed her bag and said, "I'm never going to obsess over boys the way you two do." The sound of the TV show playing in my parents' bedroom filled the small house: A beautiful girl meets the man of her dreams, but he's married. The beautiful girl and the man's wife fight over him, even though they're both unhappy; meanwhile, all he does is smoke and drink. One night, while he's drinking alone in the living room, his young daughter asks him, "Daddy, why do you drink so much?" He says, "I drink because life is hard. No one understands my pain. Don't be like your mother when you grow up." Though I'd never watched the show, I knew the whole story because their dialogue filled the house every weekend evening. When I went to class on Mondays, the other girls all talked about the show over paper cups of coffee.

"I think I'd like to marry him," my cousin said while painting clear polish onto her nails. "We haven't been dating that long, but where else am I going to meet someone like him? I can tell my mom likes him, too. Whenever he calls, she hands me the phone right away, and last week she bought me a new dress. My dad said he doesn't care who he is as long as he's not one of those protesters."

Sure enough, my cousin shows up married to the guy. I say good-bye to her at the café and am walking back to the store when I realize that, at the same time that I am impressed by her, I also feel like she's become a complete stranger to me. I feel suddenly afraid.

Yuseon is with a male customer, showing him a green button-down shirt.

"I'd prefer something plain," the customer says.

"Is this to wear to work? How about light pink? Or blue stripes?" In the end, the short, dark-skinned man buys two plain white shirts.

Right after I left home and began working at the department store, I shared a room with my friend So-yeong, who went to high school with me. My share of the rent was only 50,000 *won* a month, which was nothing, but the apartment was old with a cracked, leaky ceiling and the steep metal staircase. The heater had been broken for I don't know how many years. But it was close to the department store, so it didn't seem so bad. So-yeong, who had been living on her own since high school, was a free spirit, but she never brought guys home. At night we could look down on the lights of downtown Seoul while cars rushing along the Bugak Skyway cleaved the darkness and breezed past our apartment. Even after I saved up some money and moved out, So-yeong and her boyfriend, Hyeong-jun, would come by to invite me along for a drive.

One night, I am headed for bed, after drinking a cup of weak coffee, when So-yeong shows up at my door with a wool scarf wrapped around her face.

"Get up. We're going for a drive. Come with us."

"You mean in the truck? No way."

Hyeong-jun works at his older brother's gas station and sometimes borrows his brother's truck to take So-yeong for aimless drives on the freeway in the middle of the night. Their fervor for driving at high speeds on the fog-covered freeway and the uncomfortable bench seat that shakes mercilessly makes me nervous, so I tell her I would rather stay in and sleep.

"We're not taking the truck, dummy. We brought someone else. It's more fun if you go, too."

Since I am wearing a short-sleeved T-shirt, So-yeong covers me up with a big white cotton coat and takes me outside. Sleet is coming down, and it's very cold. Making my way carefully down the path, I see an unfamiliar car waiting at the end of the alley. So-yeong's boyfriend and a guy I don't know are sitting in the front smoking cigarettes. So-yeong keeps giggling as if something is funny. She tells Hyeong-jun, "She didn't want to come, so I had to drag her out." The car takes off quickly, even before the hem of my large coat is fully inside. Since Hyeong-jun is just a college student working at his brother's gas station and doesn't have the means to buy an imported car, I assume the new-looking Sable belongs to the driver. The wind pushes the sleet into piles along the side of the road. In the backseat, So-yeong has her arms wrapped around Hyeong-jun's neck. A gold bracelet he gave her sparkles on her wrist. He seems angry with her for some reason. Her cheerful laughter has no effect on him, and only the driver responds to her exaggerated chatter. Looking back on it now, she might have been a little drunk. "Where are we going? Isn't this the freeway?" she asks the driver. I stare hard out the window at the snowy darkness but can't tell where we are going.

So-yeong rolls the window down and sticks her head out into the snow.

"This road goes to Gugi-dong," she says. "You're not thinking of going into the mountains at this time of night, are you?"

"Why not? Is there any reason we can't hike to a mountain stream on a snowy winter night?"

Hyeong-jun unwraps So-yeong's arms from around his neck; he doesn't sound like his usual friendly self. So-yeong looks deflated.

"Remember that tall guy, Kim San-gyeong?" the driver says. "I told him we would meet him in Gugi-dong. He promised me a drink." Then he addresses me for the first time since I got in the car. "Is that okay?"

I nod, thinking I will be cold in just my short-sleeved T-shirt and cotton coat. So-yeong pouts and slouches down in her seat. The car seems to swim through the snow, which swirls in the wind, coming down like something in a painting. The driver keeps going, only the round yellow headlights of oncoming cars visible in the dark.

No one is waiting for us in Gugi-dong. It's the middle of the night and cold and snowing, so of course the trailhead is deserted.

When we get out of the car, the driver introduces himself to me.

"My name is Kim Shin-o," he says. "Does everyone want some coffee? There's a vending machine. Let's go."

He takes me with him to get coffee. The wind is quiet, and I can hear water trickling somewhere. It's too dark to see anything.

"The machine is down there, at the end," he says. He points to the other side of the road, which is lined with darkened shops. "So-yeong and Hyeong-jun were fighting the whole way to your place. She said you two used to live together. I think something's wrong with her. Hyeong-jun is quiet and doesn't talk much, but she's erratic and boy crazy."

"I thought that's why Hyeong-jun liked her in the first place," I say.

"Yeah, I suppose." He brushes the snow off his shoulders and empties his pockets of coins.

"But that's how it is. Nothing ever ends the way it begins. How could it? She should know that. We went to the same middle school, so I've known her for a long time. She has issues. The boys were all crazy about her back then. But each one who tried to date her got tired of her and gave up. That happened too often for it to be the guys' faults. But you . . ."

He pauses to look at me in the light of the vending machine.

"I heard you two are close, but you seem different. You're not like her other friends, either. You work in a department store, right?"

"That's right."

"I heard you have a boyfriend."

"Yeah."

"What does he do?"

"Nothing special. He works at a bank." I don't tell him that we just broke up.

"Now you ask me something. That's only fair."

"Do you have a girlfriend?"

"Yes, she's a year older than me. She goes to modeling school."

"Why didn't she come tonight?"

"She works the night shift at a convenience store."

"How long have you been dating?"

"Around six months."

"What kind of things do you fight about?"

"Hmm. I guess we fight about things like showing up late for dates, her borrowing my credit card and buying a suit from Anne Klein, or me staying out all night drinking with another girl. Nothing serious."

He lifts the paper cup and smiles, his white teeth visible in the dark. We see the headlights of another car coming up the mountain.

"That's San-gyeong. He said he was bringing his new girlfriend." He gulps down his coffee. "San-gyeong's a great guy. He loves places like this. Like forest trails on a winter night. He likes going places where no one else would think of going. He's a cool guy."

The guy named San-gyeong is tall and wearing glasses. He looks like he might have been the star player on his high school basketball team. The girl he introduces as his new girlfriend has dyed, bobbed hair and wears boots and earrings, but she looks like a little kid.

"She's not in elementary school, is she? Where does he find them so young?" Hyeong-jun whispers to Shin-o.

Sitting in the backseat with a sad look on her face, So-yeong takes a cup of coffee from Shin-o and mutters to me, "I think Hyeong-jun and I are going to break up. I don't think he's in love with me anymore. I should date my boss instead. This is no fun. I'm depressed."

So-yeong works as a clerk for a small trading company.

"Want to go into the forest and have some drinks there?" San-gyeong asks, sticking his head in the car.

"In this snow? No, not with the girls," Shin-o objects.

"Then maybe we can find something closer," San-gyeong says, "where we can get out of the snow. I brought the alcohol. Isn't this great? Drinking in the snow?"

"If we go down to the parking lot, the buildings should give us some cover from the snow. But don't you think it'll be too cold?" Hyeong-jun sulks.

I sip my coffee and think about the fact that if I didn't have the day off tomorrow, I would tell So-yeong to take me home that instant. The quiet, snowy night reminds me of the story of the Little Match Girl. San-gyeong takes a bottle of Rémy Martin and a stack of paper cups out of the car.

"What? You dragged us all the way out here in this weather just to drink that?" So-yeong, who's been keeping quiet, pouts, and Hyeong-jun shrugs as if he's sick of her and turns his back. I don't know what San-gyeong's young girlfriend is so happy about, but she keeps hanging on his arm and giggling.

Shin-o warns her to keep it down. "People live here," he says. "We can't make too much noise." The parking lot in front of the shuttered stores is empty, and the second floor of the buildings juts out, offering us some shelter. Shin-o finds a stack of newspapers and spreads them out. The snow is constant but turns to rain the moment it touches the asphalt. Up on the road, cars are speeding into a darkened tunnel.

San-gyeong's girlfriend reads the racing section of the Sunday sports paper that's spread out on the ground. She doesn't seem interested in anyone but San-gyeong. Each time she turns her head, her shiny hair gives off a clean smell like ice just pulled from the freezer. She leans against San-gyeong's shoulder, plays with his hair, and stares at us in defiance. *I'm just here,* her eyes say. *I'm just here and it's none of your business. Stay away from me. Don't even look at me.*

"What's your name?" Shin-o asks her as he pours the Rémy Martin into the paper cups. Hyeong-jun eats some cold fried chicken he had wrapped in tinfoil.

San-gyeong lights a bundle of the remaining newspapers with his lighter. The dry paper quickly catches fire. "Ah, that's warm."

So-yeong takes her arm from around Hyeong-jun's waist and holds her hands up to the flame. Now she really looks like the Little Match Girl. In the light of the burning newsprint, Hyeong-jun and So-yeong's faces resemble a scene from a movie. Her long hair dips forward. She looks like she's crying. Behind them, the falling snow is like a movie set.

San-gyeong's girlfriend takes the almost full cup of Rémy Martin that

Shin-o pours for her and downs it like it's Coca-Cola. "Autumn," she says.

"Your name is Autumn?"

"Yeah. Kim Autumn."

"I guess your little sister must be named Spring."

"I don't have a little sister."

"Are you in middle school?"

"What're you talking about? I'll be done with high school in another year."

The newspaper burns all the way down. Dark ash blows around on the wind and dirties the clean-swept pavement in front of the ski shop. At ten in the morning, the first of the white-shirted employees to arrive will grumble, wet a mop, and come out to clean it up. He'll sweep up the color ads and torn racing pages of the Sunday paper and throw away the empty Rémy Martin bottle and crumpled paper cups full of cigarette butts.

So-yeong buries her head in her arms. San-gyeong gets cans of beer from the car. So-yeong seems drunk, so I drink the rest of the Rémy Martin in her cup. San-gyeong and Hyeong-jun talked about the horse races they went to last Sunday.

"It was amazing," Hyeong-jun says excitedly.

"Yeah," San-gyeong agrees, "Hundred and fifty to one. But mine came in last." Shin-o offers Autumn another beer. She taps her feet and hums an old Engelbert Humperdinck song: *Please release me, let me go.* So-yeong's tears fall onto her arms.

"Don't take this the wrong way," So-yeong whispers. "It isn't Hyeong-jun's fault. He doesn't mean anything to me anymore. He doesn't make me sad, but he doesn't make me happy, either. That's how it started, and that's how it'll end."

I didn't make Hyeong-jun sad or happy, either. But it also didn't occur to me to tell him, "Let's stop seeing each other. I can't do this anymore. Not like this," when I was pulling on my stockings in the window of a hotel room overlooking the banks of a river wet with dew. Instead, I said, "I'm lonely, and it hurts." I told him, "I wanted so badly to be smothered with love that I thought I would go crazy."

"When was that?" he asked, while knotting his tie.

"When I was six."

"Were you precocious? Or just pathetic?"

"Both, probably."

"I wanted to have sex so badly, I thought I would go crazy."

"When was that?"

"Second year of high school."

I stared at the back of his white dress shirt. The smell of wet grass in the morning drifted in through the open window. The fog was slowly lifting from the highway that led back to Seoul. He slipped on his shoes with one hand and fumbled with the other for the pack of cigarettes on the table littered with half-drunk glasses of flat beer, lipstick-stained cigarette butts, and crumpled napkins and put it in his pocket. The high school sophomore who thought he'd go crazy from lack of sex and the six-year-old girl who'd suffered from a terminal lack of affection walked hand in hand out of the hotel.

Shin-o asks me to go with him to buy more beer.

"We drank everything San-gyeong brought. There's a convenience store a block that way. We can get something to eat, too."

I borrow So-yeong's scarf and tie it around my head, then stick my hands in my coat pockets and walk beside Shin-o. Past a shuttered fast-food restaurant, a shop that sells pottery fired on-site in gas kilns, and a golf shop, we see the lights of the convenience store. The employee is setting a large black plastic trash bag on the curb. The snow is still falling, but everything looks damp and dreary. If anyone were to wake up at that moment and glance out their window to see the two of us walking down the street, they wouldn't be able to get back to sleep and would have to have a smoke.

"Do you have a cigarette?" I hold out my hand to Shin-o.

"Here you go." Shin-o lights up a cigarette, takes a drag, and passes it to me. I stop in the street to smoke. The snow is slowly turning to rain.

"If the two of them break up," Shin-o says, "I might never see So-yeong again. In fact, I'm sure of it."

He pulls his jacket collar up around his neck and stuffs his hands into his jean pockets.

"Why not? You went to school together."

"Yes, but we weren't that close. Hyeong-jun's my friend, and she's his girl-friend. That's it. He's been tired of her for a while now. Lately they fight every time they see each other."

Shin-o lights another cigarette. In the headlights of an oncoming car, his profile is silhouetted like a black-and-white movie poster.

"Were you ever interested in her?" I ask.

"Briefly, in middle school. Everyone liked her back then."

It feels good to stand on a wet street late at night in a white cotton coat and smoke a cigarette while looking at the lights of a convenience store across the street. If only I could shake this anxiety about the fact that winter is com-ing. I can't spend the rest of my life thinking only about seaside bungalows and fruit cocktail with sand in it and sunlight reflecting off sunglasses.

"It was just a crush. By the way, I thought So-yeong was the one who needed a drink, but it looked like you were drinking more than her," Shin-o says as we enter the convenience store.

We buy several cans of beer, smoked dried squid, potato chips, and warm canned coffee. The cashier has the radio turned on low to keep himself awake. "Ne Me Quitte Pas" is playing.

I listen as Shin-o whistles along to the song and then ask him, "If your girlfriend works the night shift, when do you get to see each other?"

"Oh, I'll see her in five hours. I said I'd give her a ride home." He checks his watch. "She likes it when I drive her home. Even though it's only two subway stops away. We usually stop on the way for a bowl of *haejangguk*, or listen to music in the car, or have a smoke together."

"I don't know if it's a good idea for a girl to work at night. Didn't you say she wants to be a model? She must complain that it's bad for her skin."

"Of course she complains. She took the job thinking it was only temporary. But I don't think she has what it takes to be a model. She'll be lucky if she can get the occasional catalog job. Basically, she's not that pretty. Also, she's not the type to work hard at it."

"Is the Sable yours?"

"No," he says and frowns. "The truth is I work at a repair shop. I'm just a regular employee. My girlfriend thinks my dad's the owner and I own several cars, but it's not true. That car belongs to a customer. It's not mine. What kind of grease monkey owns a Sable? That's ridiculous."

"But, wait. Are you allowed to take their cars out of the shop?"

"I have to take it right back after I drop her off. Otherwise, it'll be reported as stolen."

"Why didn't you just tell her the truth?"

"San-gyeong set us up. He said it just slipped out when he was telling her about me. I didn't think it would matter, so I didn't say anything. But I'm not going to be a grease monkey forever. Absolutely not."

The second time I saw him, he told me, "I'm just an ordinary bank employee," while knotting his tie. It was that hour of the morning when manual laborers began swarming the market streets in search of a drink to chase their hangovers. From between the half-open curtains, I saw the bright, wide street filled with a procession of bicycles headed for the morning shift at a factory. Was this really the same Seoul? I had marveled over it for a moment.

"When I was in high school," he said, "I wanted to be a rock and roll singer, but it didn't go anywhere. I never once joined in any protests or demonstrations in college. But my mom still favors me. I have two older brothers, but she lets me do whatever I want, and she still calls me her baby."

I had washed my hair and was putting on eye shadow and lipstick. I still had plenty of time before I had to go to work. This man who was so interested in me even though we'd only met twice felt like a stranger to me.

"Tell me about yourself," he said as he started the car. "Tell me what you like, what you want to do."

"I like having a cigarette and a cup of coffee in the morning. And I like watching the rain through a big plate-glass window."

"Is that all?"

"Yes, that's all."

"What about what you want to do in the future?"

"Oh, that?" I stared resentfully at Wonhyo Bridge, which was getting backed up with the start of rush hour. "I don't think about the future. You said you don't, either. All I think about is death."

"Are you listening to me?" Shin-o taps me lightly on the arm.

"Huh, what did you say? The headlights are so bright, they're distracting."

"I heard you like to draw. So-yeong told me. So you want to become an artist?"

"I'm a complete amateur. I wanted to go to art school but couldn't, so now I'm just doing it as a hobby."

In the parking lot, San-gyeong and Hyeong-jun are burning newspapers like a pair of hobos. So-yeong has cheered back up and is giggling with Autumn. So-yeong's pale arms rest on Hyeong-jun's shoulder like a phantom. Her gold bracelet sparkles in the light of the flames. *I don't think about the future. All I think about is death.* Did I really say that to him?

My cousin starts dropping by the department store to chat, claiming that she's only there to pick up an Arpeggione Sonata CD or a pink cotton bathrobe to wear after a bath. Sometimes she comes by when I'm getting off work, and we go out for steak. So-yeong shows up, too, sometimes. After she breaks up with Hyeong-jun, she starts wearing a red suit and high heels with her hair pulled into an updo, and I almost don't recognize her. So-yeong says my cousin is the type of woman who will plunk her baby down in front of *Sesame Street* as soon as it's born. Maybe, I say. But So-yeong has also stopped wearing torn blue jeans like a back-alley hippie. What's more, she tells me that she's started getting regular facials.

"Are you dating your boss now?" I ask.

She responds by laughing cynically.

"What's he like?" I ask.

"He's a snob."

"A bourgeois pig?"

"Exactly. A perfect specimen."

She takes out her compact to check her mascara for clumps. Now that she's wearing makeup, she looks wild and beautiful. This is not the girl who climbed into Hyeong-jun's truck in sneakers and long skirts, who didn't care that her hair was tangled. She sips her cola through a straw, leaving behind a clear lipstick stain.

"How's it working out?"

"How is what working out?"

"The bank guy."

"It's not."

"You broke up, huh?"

"Yeah."

"Good. He wasn't right for you. He was completely unstable. Couldn't you tell?"

My cousin puts it a little differently.

"You need to take a good look at yourself first," she says, tapping a half-eaten piece of steak with her fork. "What I mean is that you need to figure out what you want first. Then you can move on. Actually, to tell you the truth, this is the same thing Eun-gyeong told me."

As for whether my cousin is happily married, I assume that's the case. Her "marriage" is a beautiful and successful one. Her handsome medical student still loves her, still gives her flowers and jewelry, and still takes her to see avant-garde plays on the weekends just as he did before they were married. But now, whenever she shows up at the men's suit department where I work, carrying a department store shopping bag, it seems like something in her is missing. She still has the perky, satisfied smile of a model in an ad for Italian blue jeans, but the red-cheeked girl who ran out of the old photo studio into the shining summer street has long since vanished.

"I have to move," So-yeong says one day while absentmindedly browsing the latest shirt designs from Guy Laroche. "I've stopped donating to Greenpeace, and I can't help but think that I'm turning into your cousin. I even met with a matchmaker. I might be getting married soon."

She walks around the store, examining each of the pastel-colored shirts on display like a woman shopping for a shirt for her fiancé.

"Really? Congratulations." It takes me a moment to say it, as if the words just occurred to me. "What's he like?" I add.

"He's just a regular guy. Works for the Ministry of Home Affairs. Thirty years old, second-oldest son, has a fifty-six-square-meter apartment," she adds impassively. "Mom's happy about it. She hated Hyeong-jun."

If this were a fairy tale, So-yeong's story would end there. The beautiful princess finally marries her prince and lives happily ever after—though it's a bit of a stretch to call an employee of the Ministry of Home Affairs a prince. But I sense that I'll run into So-yeong again one day. I'll see her in a park on a snowy night. She'll be sitting on the asphalt setting fire to the Sunday sports paper with a lighter. She'll watch the paper burn, her arm around Hyeong-jun's shoulder, as if nothing has changed. Even after all those years, they won't have have changed a bit.

"Are you looking for something in particular? Oh, you must be shopping for the wedding. Can I help?"

"Why are you talking about weddings already? Nothing's been decided. But," she says, gesturing toward the kitchen section upstairs, "I am looking for kitchen scissors."

"Kitchen scissors?"

"Yeah."

"That's what you came to buy?"

"I want a good pair. Something big and sturdy, and expensive. Made in Germany or Switzerland."

I assume that's not really what she's there to buy. Kitchen scissors suit her about as well as a floral-print apron, a meat tenderizer, or bathroom cleaner. All I see in the department store's full-color flyer that she holds in her hand is a picture of a woman with a kerchief on her head standing in a perfect kitchen, sipping coffee and smiling like a princess. Then I see the kichen scissors propped up in a glass on the mirrorlike table behind the woman. They look like a good pair, shiny and sturdy. I have no idea why they placed the scissors like that in an ad for a system kitchen. Maybe someone thought they completed the look. Like a single tulip in a vase. So-yeong was probably handed the flyer at the bottom of the escalator and looked at it on the way up. Then, when I asked what she was looking for, she latched onto that as her answer.

My cousin has changed, as well. She shows up carrying several huge shopping bags. A pink cotton bathrobe peeks out from one of the packages.

"I've started buying steaks here because of you," she says. "Seop is getting married. Mom tried going on a hunger strike, but it didn't work. She refuses to meet his fiancée, and the fiancée has been acting cold in turn because of it. Things are a mess at home."

"Why does your mother hate her so much? Is she from a poor family? Did she go to a bad school? Or is her mother a shaman?"

"No, nothing like that."

I get off work, and we walk through the crowded downtown shopping district, browsing through several shoe stores before stopping at a café in the lounge of one of the buildings. The weather is cold and gray and threatens to snow. The whipped cream on top of the Viennese coffee is sprinkled with cinnamon, and the cup is warm.

"She's the daughter of a college professor, and she graduated from a top women's college. That's not the problem. The problem is how much my brother has changed because of her."

Whipped cream is stuck to her lip.

"Mom wanted Seop to have the kind of marriage where you get along well and love for the sake of stability. The kind of love where he loves the woman because she looks nice, wears light nail polish, and cooks for her husband on the weekends. But this girl shook him up and turned him into a totally different person. Now he's crazy and passionate, obsessing over her every little gesture and every word she says, and then falling into despair over it. He won't listen to anyone and doesn't care what anyone thinks. He's not the kind, gentle Seop who used to be like a Harvard nerd. The changes in him have us all baffled. Mom probably feels the most betrayed."

I tell her that the first time I heard there was an issue with the woman Seop planned to marry, I assumed she was the type of woman who'd gone to night school, had a mother who was on her third marriage, and cracked her gum all the time.

"We all love Seop. You know that. I think Mom is just jealous, in a way. But not me. I think there's a tragic element to his passion. They'll probably break up eventually. Not because Mom or the rest of the family disapprove. Their crazy relationship will get to them."

Naturally, I do not go to Seop's wedding. I don't hear the news until much later, but, just as my cousin predicted, they divorce by mutual consent after a year of marriage. I don't know why. Up until I quit my job and move to another department store, my cousin continues to visit several more times. As for changing jobs, the pay is better and I don't have to work on the sales floor anymore, but also there is the matter of the scandal. All I did was go out drinking all night a few times with the young, married manager, but after his wife came to the store and made a scene, I couldn't work there anymore. Two years go by at my new job. The working conditions aren't bad, and they're forgiving about minor scandals. Nothing special happens until, one day, I get a phone call.

It is a Wednesday morning full of ennui. The weather is neither rainy nor windy. The days have been continuously overcast, as if the sky is depressed. The elevator girls, who are fresh out of high school, fill their bowls with salad in the company cafeteria in the morning and complain about their sticky foundation and melting mascara. A man next to them recommends that they try Chanel. Another man eating toast and coffee chimes in to suggest waterproof mascara. Someone points out that the department store gets more crowded when the weather is gloomy. People aren't in the mood for anything, he says, and it's a great change of scenery. Nothing better to do than to kill a cloudy afternoon at an indoor driving range. Little has changed in two years. The elevator girls' pink jackets and black pleated skirts, the scent of their Lirikos perfume bought with their employee discounts, and even the low-hung gray sky look the same as ever to me. After I arrive at my job in the credit department, I flip through the Wednesday edition of the morning paper and then drink a cup of coffee and banter lightly with the people next to me.

"I lost my credit card," the phone call begins. "My ID number is 62xxxx-xxxxxx, and my name is Kim Shin-o."

"Where did you lose it, sir?" I ask.

The monotonous rasp of file drawers opening and the tapping of key-boards fill the office. Just as they have for the past two years, everyone answers their phones in flat voices, smokers gather in the hallway to sip coffee and complain about how the office is being turned into a no-smoking zone, and women in white blouses deliberate over whether they should skip lunch to lose weight. I politely repeat the question.

"Where did you lose it, sir?"

"I lost it at a trailhead in Gugi-dong. That was two nights ago. It was a muggy, overcast night."

Kim Shin-o's personal information pops up on the screen. Occupation: auto mechanic. Family: wife, Yi Gyeong-rim; son, Yu-no. It's the same Kim Shin-o from two years ago. The same Kim Shin-o who stole a Sable and waited until dawn to give his girlfriend, who worked the night shift, a ride home. His girlfriend, the aspiring model who was convinced that he was from a rich family and had fallen for her. Shin-o had read So-yeong's tears in the dark and walked a long way with me to buy potato chips and beer. Over the phone, he tells me that So-yeong, whom I haven't seen in a long time, is dead.

"I haven't talked to you in ages," he says. "So you're still working at the department store?"

"It's a different department store than before. But they're pretty much the same."

He laughs.

"Did I tell you I'm still working at a garage?"

"I already know, including the fact that you have a son."

"Ah," he sighs. "She's great, my wife. We started dating last year, and she got pregnant right away, so we got married. She's pretty and has a good heart. Yet she never thought of becoming a model!"

We laugh together over the phone. Then he tells me about So-yeong. He says that all of his middle school friends have been talking about it.

"I thought you might not have heard. It wasn't in the papers or anything. It happened less than a month ago. It was a really hot day. The heat wave probably made the headlines."

I can tell how badly he needs a cigarette now.

"Her wrists. She slashed her wrists. With kitchen scissors."

"Kitchen scissors?"

"Yes. A brand-new pair of kitchen scissors that she bought at the department store that afternoon. They were probably expensive, the really sturdy kind."

"She called me a few times. I thought she was happy. I didn't think anything was wrong."

"Maybe she was. Or maybe not. Anyway, all that matters now is . . ."

"Is that she slashed her wrists with a pair of scissors?"

"Right. The rest is meaningless. Her husband was on his way back from the airport. He'd been out of town on business."

We hang up, and I go to lunch. In the middle of eating the cafeteria salad, which never changes, I suddenly remember what I am doing that weekend. I don't know why, but I'd momentarily forgotten. I am planning to meet someone at the domestic terminal in the airport. It might have been what Kim

Shin-o said on the phone, about someone coming back from the airport, that jogs my memory.

Someone at a table behind me is talking loudly about how she likes the color red best on gray days. It's the woman from the retail design team; she eats a tiny bowl of rice topped with tomatoes and chrysanthemum greens. She wears a plain, dark dress without so much as a red scarf wrapped around her. The thought of having to go to the airport weighs more heavily on me than the colorless weather. A woman wearing large hoop earrings and what looks like three-inch heels brushes past me and stumbles, spilling some of her *dwenjang* soup on the floor. Several new male employees walking past laugh loudly.

I think about So-yeong's wedding. The photographer, a professional whom she'd specifically hired from a photo studio downtown, wound up throwing a fit because of all the firecrackers being set off and the clumsy guests getting in his way to take their own amateur photos. Women dressed in silk *hanbok* kept going in and out of the buffet restaurant where the reception was held, while children in their Sunday best were running around looking for their mothers. Made up like Snow White, So-yeong was laughing loudly with her mouth wide-open. It must have been this time of year—it wasn't quite autumn yet, and the wind was blowing hard. A lot of young men in suits were there, including Kim Shin-o. His girlfriend, the aspiring model, must have been by his side. But I had only a faint memory of her face, as if it were shrouded in fog. I didn't remember her as being particularly memorable or striking. The fact that she wanted to be a model made her seem more glamorous than she really was. But I liked watching her long hair sway around her face each time she turned her head. Shin-o was more enamored with her than anyone else. As the pianist played the wedding march, the bride and groom walked down the aisle together, covered with white streamer spray. At the reception, the groom, who was a government employee with the Ministry of Home Affairs, walked around pouring glasses of champagne for the guests. Someone sang an old song that began, *I'm a gentle lamb because I love you. My heart frolics in the meadow of your bosom.*

I decided to go to the airport after a lot of hesitation, and even then I barely agreed to it.

I stand in the window of my room sipping coffee. It is evening, and a soft, humid breeze is blowing. Autumn is still a ways off. I smell bread baking in a bakery in the alley below. I slowly sip my coffee and debate whether I should put on my jacket and go downstairs to buy one of the warm Danish pastries that I like, or just stay put. The phone rings. I hesitate but end up picking up the phone. Lately, my cousin has come to enjoy telling me all about one of her husband's coworkers. She called once to tell me she thought about me while buying a wool Burberry sweater for herself last winter. She probably thinks I am lonely.

"So I decided to give you the sweater instead," she'd said. "I'm not sure why you were on my mind. I guess I just think you should hurry up and get married."

The evening air fills with the scent of warm bread floating in through the open second-floor window. The display designer wanted me to meet him at the airport. "You can get time off?"

I'd wondered aloud. "I should be able to." Once his business trip in the provinces was over, he would have about a week to himself.

"You're twenty-seven," my cousin says impatiently. "This might be your last chance. He's a doctor. He'll keep you in comfort. Don't you want to take it easy?"

The designer wants to date but isn't interested in marrying me. My cousin hates him.

"You can live without him, can't you? You're just lonely. You're afraid of being alone. I get it."

She tells me that even when she's getting her hair done at the salon, the mere thought of him can make her upset.

"I just wanted to make sure you really exist," the designer had said over the phone. "I haven't been able to sleep at all since yesterday. I feel strange. My head is stuffed up. I wish you would come to the airport." I wound up promising him I would.

I sweep the dust from the carpet and close the window. Then I put some piano music on in the CD player, clean the bathroom, and take some frozen orange juice out to dilute it with mineral water.

At work, one of the elevator girls who had just come into the cafeteria yelled that she didn't want to become an old maid. "It's not that I want to get married, I just don't want to be an old maid." She was twenty-two and had gotten engaged to one of the managers earlier that year. She had big, innocent-looking eyes and long eyelashes. She pushed her boiled cabbage around her plate and asked me whether I was lonely. The other female employees sitting nearby either pretended not to listen and kept eating or exchanged sly looks with each other.

"No, I have a boyfriend. If that's what you mean, then I'm not lonely."

Her innocent-looking eyes widened. "Oh no, do you mean that guy from the display design team you were sitting with in the sky lounge last time? I heard he never wants to get married." One of the long-haired women sitting next to her broke down and started tittering. A half-peeled summer tangerine fell off her tray and rolled across the floor.

I stand in the waiting room of the domestic terminal and watch cars pull in and out of the lot. It's a Saturday, so they're all coming from weddings and are festooned with balloons and ribbons. It's an unusually clear day. The sunlight filling the parking lot reminds me of the flames that rose from the newspaper that dark night in the parking lot near the trailhead. So-yeong's white arm with its gold bracelet wrapped around Hyeong-jun's shoulders. It is almost September, but the sunlight beating down on the parking lot is mercilessly bright. A small bride in a white dress walks through the glare toward the terminal with her groom and their friends. Her white silk dress, the white stockings, and the sweltering white sunlight wash her out. Someone has playfully spelled out the words *I love you* in English with red tape on her white honeymoon suitcase.

"I don't care. I am getting on that plane," says a girl on the plastic bench next to me. She is wearing a white floral-print dress and dark sunglasses. She is talking to the guy next to her. They are each holding a can of 7UP with straws in them. The guy's head is turned, and I cannot see his expression, so I can't tell if he's angry. He hangs his head. He takes her hand. But she enunciates each word again clearly. "I am getting on that plane. Don't try to stop me. I don't want to leave on bad terms." The world collapses silently around them.

There was a lot of time left over after I finished breakfast, but I left for the airport anyway. I think about how many hours I will have to wait and start to feel bored. Women dressed in shiny *hanbok* with flowers in their hair, carrying colorful bouquets and clinging to men's arms, parade past me. A couple sits down across from me on a plastic bench instead of going to board a plane. The woman is wearing a purple dress that looks like it went out of style a long time ago and chocolate-colored shoes with low heels. The man is turned toward the stainless steel ashtray to tap out his cigarette. I am debating whether to go get another cup of coffee from the vending machine when I see the man's profile. It's the man I broke up with over the phone two years ago after talking to him about green apples for the last time. He doesn't look a day older, and nothing else about him has changed. He doesn't see me. The woman in the purple dress gets up and goes to the bathroom. They don't look like they're on their honeymoon, nor do they seem to be traveling far. He looks like he hasn't shaved in a while, and his dress shirt is wrinkled, which makes him look tired and as if deep in thought about something. I feel relieved that he doesn't recognize me, but also a little disappointed.

I get up and go to the bathroom. A girl is standing right up against the mirror, combing her long hair with her fingers and staring into her own eyes. I grab a paper towel, wet it with lukewarm tap water, wipe off the eye shadow that now seems too heavy, and reapply a dark pink lipstick. I look at myself in the mirror and go back in time two years. I am leaning out the window of a car racing down a highway in late autumn in order to get a better look at the windy, deserted fields. While my heart pounds at the dry, expressionless eyes of the woman selling green apples on the side of the road, at the strangeness and desolation of that woman, I grab a green-colored pencil and start sketching those apples that we bought in their brown paper bag. That road with its green apples, as pale as the worn-out sunlight and as depressing as the piano music that played in the car. Wait. Was it piano music? Or was it just a pop song on the radio? Some singer whose voice sounded like Jeon In-kwon's? A piano sonata that started off monotonous and boring but rose to a thundering climax. Hadn't I heard that kind of piano music long before that? In some shadowy basement bar in midsummer? A woman in a blue dress was playing piano onstage. Outside, the sun had long set, but the weather was so hot and humid that it felt like the clouds would burst at any moment. But inside, a large portable air conditioner was running, and the girls were sipping sticky sweet vodka sunrises through straws. It was dark in the bar, and I couldn't see anyone's face through the cigarette smoke and the dry ice evaporating on the plate of pineapple on the table. The woman in the blue dress started singing. I didn't recognize the song. The tone and rhythm reminded me of a French chanson. It was sometime in the summer, and the bar was the sort of place where girls would work part-time even before they were out of high school so that they could make money to go to the beach. Or maybe I was remembering it all wrong. The bar with the piano might have happened long after that day I bought green apples on the west coast highway. The languid piano music made the stifling dark of the basement weigh even heavier, and the pianist in the blue dress was putting her hair up and fixing it in place with a pin. The girls might have been drinking Bloody Marys, not vodka sunrises, and there might have been popcorn crumbs scattered all over the tables and floor. I was one of those girls wearing a sleeveless white dress that left my shoulders bare. I was there to meet the designer, and the rest of my memories were a jumble. The one thing I did remember clearly was that piano playing over and over like a broken record. The same piano music I heard in the car on the highway in late autumn.

I hear a toilet flush, and the woman in the purple dress comes out of the stall. She touches up her bangs in front of the mirror, takes out a light-colored lipstick from her bag, and applies it. Her outfit is conspicuously out of style, but up close, her face is surprisingly pretty. Her wide, beautiful eyes twinkle, and her cheeks look like peaches. She seems young. The girl who has been doing nothing but staring at herself in the mirror goes over to the window and lights a cigarette. The woman in the purple dress leaves. I hear the steady drip of water from a faucet that hasn't been turned off all the way. An airport announcement states that the flight for Busan is departing soon. I want a cigarette. When I come out, he is alone. The woman in the purple dress is gone.

"She's not coming back," he tells me. "She's gone back home."

We sit across from each other at the airport grill and drink lemonade. Inside, the sweet aroma of air freshener and the smell of hot coffee mixes with the scent of thick slices of lightly toasted bread. The restaurant is also filled with waves of newlyweds waiting for their planes.

"I'm glad to see you're doing well," he says.

A silver ashtray sits on top of the tablecloth, which has a faint coffee stain. He lights a cigarette.

"Last week my washing machine broke, and before that, someone offered me a good price on a used Yamaha piano, but I had to let it go since my room is so small. I also had to call a repairman twice because of the heater. But aside from that, I'm doing well," I say.

"My job at the bank is one headache after another." He frowns. "I used to drink every night before going to bed. I had this friend in high school—I think about him each time I drink. I haven't seen him in ages. He moved to a fishing village on the south coast after college. Or was it the west coast? That's right, I remember now. It was the west coast."

Though he looks tired and worn-down at twenty-seven, his profile is as handsome as ever, and he has the attractiveness of someone who's just come in from playing tennis.

"I'm waiting for someone," I say, and check my watch. He will be here soon. "Who?"

"A designer from the department store. He went on a business trip to one of the regional branches."

"Are you meeting him for work?"

"No."

We sit together anyway for five more minutes as we drink the last of our lemonade, which is watered down from the melting ice, and smoke the cigarettes down to their filters. Finally, I ask him about the woman.

"That woman in the purple dress was very pretty."

He smiles faintly.

"So are you," he says. "When I was with you, my friends at the bank were so jealous. She used to work as a teller at the same branch as me. She's nice. Probably because she's still such a country girl."

"I have to go now," I say. I smooth the wrinkles out of my skirt as I stand up.

As I'm walking away, I hear him ask, "Can I call you sometime at the department store?"

His plane lands on time, and we have no problem catching a cab. The weather is very hot, but the sky is blue and the sunlight as sharp as glass. My rented room has a tiny balcony with a nice view. I had thought about lying out there on a towel in my bathing suit with my Walkman in my ears so that I could get a tan. All I needed was a pair of sunglasses, oil, and an Agatha Christie novel. I had worked all summer long without going to the beach. I'd gotten tired of trying to get the other girls at work together for a trip to the beach, and I was too self-conscious to try to get the same vacation days as the designer. He had gone to Jeju Island with his friends and come back with an enormous pineapple.

That night, the designer and I, along with several of his friends from work, go to a basement bar. I keep switching between vodka sunrises and straight whiskey. After a while, I get pretty drunk. Onstage, a long-haired woman in a blue dress plays the piano. Large pieces of pineapple sit in a glass dish on the table. The men loosen their neckties, and the girls order large bowls of ice. I'm certain I've been in a basement bar on a summer night like this before. The thunderous piano music, the shadowy figures in the dark, the large portable air conditioner quietly humming. Everything is so familiar, but I cannot remember when I've seen it all before. The men are talking about work, and I am on my fifth glass of whiskey.

As the night progresses, one of them suggests going up to the sky lounge on the top floor. "There's an express elevator. The lounge looks out over the Han River."

Someone else says, "What's so great about that? We see the river every day. I like the music here."

In the end, we all go up to the sky lounge and have martinis. The view of the Han River at night and the cars driving along the highway is beautiful.

"I have a gift for you," he tells me.

An evening breeze comes in through the open balcony door. It carries the scent of the river. I am sitting on a round cushion, jiggling my leg, and smoking a cigarette. I'm a little queasy, but the cool breeze in the darkened hotel room makes me feel better. The designer takes out a box of Godiva chocolates and pink Chanel lipstick.

"The salesgirl said it's waterproof. And that it won't smudge. I picked a color you wear a lot."

"Thank you."

I start to feel queasy again, so I go out onto the balcony. Far below, I can see the lights of the hotel parking lot.

"You're not going to throw up out there, are you?" he asks. "I think you had too much to drink."

"So what if I throw up? Anyway, I feel better now. I'll just stay out here a little longer."

I feel like I've had one too many whiskeys. The side of my head is pounding.

"They gave me something at the department store. A kitchen utensil set or something. You can have it."

He takes a box wrapped in shiny black paper out of his suitcase.

"I live with my mom and don't cook for myself, so I don't know why they gave me this."

I look inside the box lying open on the table. He says proudly, "See, it's the new German kitchen set." A pair of shiny silver kitchen scissors made by Henckels rests on the table. There are other things, too, of course. Measuring spoons, a fruit knife, a trivet for hot pots, and a fancy kitchen scale. The scissors look sturdy and strong.

"You don't mind this, right?" he asks.

We are in bed. The scissors are just sitting there on the table. I hear a crackling sound coming from the river. Someone must be setting off fireworks.

"What do you mean by 'this'?" I ask.

"I mean going on dates and having sex and talking on the phone. Going out to the hotel lounge at the Sheraton Walkerhill now and then. I was worried you might get tired of it. I want to do what you want to do." He plays with my hair and then falls asleep. The Godiva chocolates, each one individually wrapped in pretty silver paper, are scattered across the table and the carpeted floor. I unwrap one of the chocolates and pop it in my mouth. It tastes like a dried leaf or overcooked cabbage. I go out onto the balcony and lean over the railing. Dawn is coming. Some eager person somewhere must already be warming up for a jog.

At the airport, I should have asked him about the highway with green apples. Then he would have searched his memory and said: *To get there, you just have to take a train and then transfer to a bus. There's a river and a lake nearby. Once you're on the highway, go straight until you reach the ocean.*

The scissors continue to shine among the cans of coffee, chocolates, and various kitchen utensils sitting on top of the table. I have had too much whiskey. I light a cigarette and drink a half-full can of lukewarm coffee. To the final darkness of summer before the oncoming dawn, I whisper: "I don't know anything." I'm not thrilled by sex, and I'm not moved by love. I gaze down at the road stretching off into the distance and stand still in the bleak, dusty wind. I think I can smell the green of the river and the scent of old grass. "Is the ocean this way?" they pull over and ask. The wind ruffles my hair and flattens the tall, dry grass along the side of the road. Rachmaninov blares out the car windows, and they buy green apples.

About the Author

BAE SUAH was born in Seoul in 1965. After majoring in chemistry as an undergrad, she became a writer at the relatively late age of twenty-eight. Her first short story, which she wrote while learning how to type on a word processor, was published in a literary magazine. Prior to that, she had never taken any creative writing or literature classes. *Highway with Green Apples*, published in Korean in 1995 and making its English debut here, is one of her first works. She continued to publish over the years, and in 2001, she moved to Berlin, where she took a break from writing to learn German. In 2008, she began translating German literature into Korean, beginning with Martin Walser's *Angstblüte*. She has also translated two works by W. G. Sebald, one of her favorite German writers (*Nach der Natur* and *Schwindel. Gefühle,* both forthcoming). She is also a fan of the Portuguese writer Fernando Pessoa and is currently translating *The Book of Disquiet*.

About the Translator

SORA KIM-RUSSELL is a literary translator based in Seoul. Her translations of Kyung-sook Shin's *I'll Be Right There* and Gong Ji-young's *Our Happy Time* are forthcoming in 2014. She teaches at Ewha Womans University.

UPON FIRST LOOKING INTO A HIGH SCHOOL PHOTOGRAPHY EXHIBITION INSIDE A STRIP MALL

BY JEFF BAKER

Any horse, when grazing, becomes a stellar
target. A kitten's default mode
is unroustable slumber. The elderly long ago
became masters of the sedentary.
Yet one sophomore named Trish has hung
a big muddled time-lapse
of an umbrella magnolia opening—a work
she has titled *Self-portrait*.
After a long stare, I begin to sense a blurred
sway of petals loosed by light.
I'm convinced I can see the first curious car
meandering on the freeway
of the bee—see dew's crystal reflective scoops
apparitioning to vapor.
Does Trish not pose a treacly truth? Don't we
all pour too much of our was
and will-be into now's spilt thimble? Aren't
we walking chronologies that
cannot keep our place? The adolescent face

of an octogenarian might be seen
within a prankish glance, or the too-young
    bride on her wedding day might
well appear at the funeral upon the widow's
        face. Isn't there a multitude
staring out from every mirrored gaze, from
        yellowed photos trapped
inside their frames? To take it further, Trish,
    consider: each particle of light
is from a separate age—photons born twenty
        thousand, a hundred thousand,
a million years ago during fusion in the sun's
        dense core, all escaped its gravity
at once eight minutes past to just now together
        penetrate this strip mall glass
and illuminate *Self-portrait*. So we're all like you
        Trish, in that our faces drift
in this polytemporal light, ancient simultaneity
        of light, which we might
erroneously refer to as *Now*. If we could truly
        time-lapse *Now*, Trish, would
that require each moment of every life—every
        stumped toe and car crash, every
marriage and execution? In *Now's Self-portrait*,
        the octogenarian's mother cries
out in labor just as his daughter is leaning over
        the coffin to kiss his folded hands.
Now the age spots dappling his dead wrists are
        being loaded onto the helixes that
made him. *Now* all the widow's incarnations
        turn light back into every eye

that ever glimpsed her as her hand grasps
the rounded doorknob—her
excarnation waiting one turn away. Or, flung
open now, Trish, the strict
modality of the hearse as we together look
gawkish past the windshield's
wipers at the spectrum of visible us. We whose
genome holds the history
of a species and all our possibilities. We who
were once fire-flung stumps
of carbon cooked in a dying sun. We finites
neverending. We troves
of happening. We innumerable hives humming
with familiar ghosts. We holds.
We echoes. We harmonies. We everlasting Trish
adrift in the lacteal wash of stars.

About the Author

Originally from a place called Smokey Branch in East Tennessee, JEFF BAKER has earned degrees from Tennessee Tech and the Iowa Writers' Workshop. A collection of his poems, *Whoop and Shush*, was selected by Dorianne Laux for the Idaho Poetry Prize and is forthcoming from Lost Horse Press in early 2015. His poems have recently appeared in *Copper Nickel*, *Washington Square* and *Blackbird*, and have been anthologized in *Best New Poets 2010* and *The Southern Poetry Anthology, Volume VI: Tennessee*.

Keith Carter © 2013

Brooke Weeber © 2014

SMALL BOTTLES

THEO SCHELL-LAMBERT

I can't stand flying in unfamiliar airplanes. Whenever I finally get used to an engine noise—the lactic French grumble of an Airbus A319, that high cajole of a 737—I find myself sitting on a taxiway in Fayetteville or Frankfort in some old MD-80, and I realize I haven't flown McDonnell Douglas in years, and I'm about to spend the whole flight trying to figure out if the jet whine is supposed to sound like that or if it's two troubling ticks too nasal.

I'm always calmed when I open the equipment specs in the seatback pocket—and they're always there, if you check, addressed like postcards to men like me—and discover we're running on a Rolls-Royce power plant. Not only does it feel like finery on the cheap, a little English alliteration to hang your hat on during a juddering jump from Dallas to Des Moines, but I also have a theory that you should always trust a luxury brand, even outside its area of expertise. They know how to cover their bases. They don't want to do something to you that will embarrass them. I used to own Beretta jackets. I used to stick small bottles where the shotgun shells should go. I don't own them anymore.

Lately I've been getting a tour of America's aging fleets—her off-brand carriers, those hermaphroditic jets they send to hop you from one Midwestern city to the next. Canadairs and Bombardiers and Dash 8s. Embryonic

Embraers. I have Saab stories. I know that sad feeling of stooping through the fuselage door and turning right to see you've pulled a 2-and-1, and you won't be able to hold your head up till Rockford.

I used to fly in twin-aisles, even nationally. That's when you know you've made it. When they give you room to breathe even on the short haul. I'd wing from Chicago to San Francisco in the bulkhead seat of a 767, four, six times a month. I'd earn enough miles after three months to score two frequent-flier seats to San Juan, earn enough revenue for the company that they'd send me there for free anyway, not to mention hand me the perk at a sales conference in Miami that was a vacation on its own. I'd forget that under-seat storage even existed. Sometimes, if the latitude was low and the schedule light, I'd bring my wife and daughter along, taking pleasure in the prime number on their tickets, the prime real estate out the window. Their view was the coastline, and my view was them. Looking back, I should have brought them along every time, flown them east, west, due north in coach.

The map of that old landscape languishes in my brain. Those farms and lakes and oceans that used to spread themselves out just for me. I don't like the view anymore. A couple years ago I stopped looking out the window altogether. Now I make a point to score the window seat just so I can make sure that it's snapped shut, that I don't wind up next to some curious fool in 9A who insists on exposing our whole row to all that's down there.

Back then I was still living in one of those proper cities, the kind of place you don't wonder about when you see it from thirty thousand feet, orange and pulsing. You just know it's someplace real. I had my wife and daughter, and I had a house made of quarried stone, and I had a base salary that skipped like a rock off my checking account and went straight into investment-grade securities, the product I was selling was that good. I could live for a year off the commissions I made in the first quarter. I could walk into a room with a blazing hotel-bar hangover and settle a deal on impatience alone.

In all those years, I don't think I ever took the turn into the F terminal at my home airport, the sad ground-level corridor for the small carriers. I never had to find out how far the alphabet went. Now every week I wander through those ghettos, those Gs and Hs that don't sound like airport letters at all. Watching twentysomething pilots and fiftysomething stewardesses flirt over a vending-machine dinner. Thinking how those Munchos and that Reese's have to power us to Racine.

Half those terminals don't even have a proper bar, which irks me from a standpoint of taste and services, but I have to admit it's probably what's keeping me aloft. I suppose I owe something to those bare lounges, all those sodden turkey sandwiches, those soiled chairs with the fixed armrests so that I can't even lie down and dream my way out of there. They keep me right where I am.

It has not escaped my notice that back when I was in those proper fliers' bars, with a heavy cut glass in my hand, with something clearer than water in the glass, I was trying to depart a place that I should have been clinging to with both arms.

———

I sell a bad product now. That's what they give you when you prove yourself not sufficiently appreciative of the good. They demote you from the modern virtual goods, the flyweight pills and ideas. You leave the lovely world of cloud storage and are walked over to a warehouse full of unwieldy items, improbable shapes. All at once, everything exists in hard copy again. There are actual objects, and the kicker is that you can misplace them. They are not backed up. You had forgotten all about that. You had forgotten that in the twenty-first century it was still possible to lose things.

My old stuff wasn't physical, no sample case required. I wasn't hawking pharmaceuticals, exactly, but it was a little like that. It might as well have been Prozac or Lipitor, the way I was hustling people with a vision of who they could be, a way to change without changing at all. It's tempting now to fault those old easy sellers, the promises that came out of my mouth every afternoon. You can't fly a 777 to Wichita Falls, and you can't change without changing. Can you blame a man shilling that kind of magic for thinking he could have it all?

I asked my boss that very question, the day two years ago that he called me into his office. He seemed to think you could.

Those sweet easy sellers were a world away from this product that's teetering at my feet right now. It always looks like it's about to tip over, but that's just how it looks. I have to haul it with me wherever I go, crammed inside a roller duffel that's four inches in every direction too big for carry-on. I long ago gave up trying to stuff it into the sizer at check-in. If the bag were just one total foot smaller, my whole traveling life would be different. I wouldn't burn away my tiny evenings next to claim carousels, making myself plead with representatives not to let it stay lost. Naturally these new bag fees come right out of my pocket. Sometimes I think I'm no longer a salesman at all, that the airlines have gotten together to run a sale on me.

Then I lug that heavy bag to the next hotel, and that same yellow smoking room I'm reclining in now, as I press a pack of ice against my face. I always hate the smell, but my first move is always lighting up a Marlboro Medium and producing more of it for the next traveler. It strokes my nerves. A "medium" cigarette, a real hedging of vices. And as soon as I've dashed out the butt, I do the thing I must, which is check the minifridge to make sure they've heeded my call and cleared it of tiny bottles. Just once they hadn't, and even though I hadn't sold a thing in weeks, I didn't wait for the front desk to come pull them out. Maybe I just couldn't stand to watch them do it. Immediately, one after the next, I slung each of the dozen whiskeys and vodkas and beloved gins from the eighth-floor window and watched them smash onto the frozen parking lot. Mixed a Long Island Iced Tea right there on the Iowa asphalt. Then I rode back downstairs and paid in cash for what I'd done.

But usually there is no big drama. Just that horribly empty refrigerator door. I wish they'd put something else in there, extra sodas or even food or candy or something, anything. Some drinkers' ready pack of Fresca and stale crackers and ice-cold Skittles. On especially dire nights I've been known to put the little shampoos and conditioners in the door just so I don't have to think about the missing shapes. Right now, just ten feet from my feet there are four fresh Avedas cooling. A little oil in my hair is a small price to pay. So much of what makes an airplane, a bottle, feel good is just the familiar dimensions.

At least I sleep better now, most of the time. The sleep takes years to come, but once it arrives, it carries me through one night. Not like in the flush days when I'd pass out with ease, swinging in a ménage à trois with my steady buzz and some new woman, then wake up four hours later, both partners long gone. I would lie there for long minutes staring at the phone, trying to figure out if it was ringing. In the beginning, I would hope desperately that it wasn't, but it always was. A boss, a wife, a representative from the airline, curious why I'd missed the meeting, the T-ball game, the 11:00 a.m. to Houston. Even my flight times used to be so dignified, ending in those crisp zeros. The only watch I needed was the latest gleaming Movado I'd won in Miami, brazenly lacking the hour and minute markers. They give them to the best salesmen because the best salesmen don't need to know.

Eventually, I got my wish. Eventually, the phone wasn't ringing. When I got put on bad products, my first wake-up call was that my old watch was useless. I offered it to a retiring rep who'd bequeathed me his best lines, and he just laughed. "What's the point of a watch that can't tell time?"

———

They say you have to hit rock bottom, but in my experience enough hard scrapes of the landing gear will do. Until the day I actually felt the ground, I thought I wasn't buying the farm. One thing less seasoned fliers don't realize is that you can accumulate a crash landing over time.

On a Wednesday morning in Atlanta, the ringing telephone was real, and on a Monday afternoon in Memphis it was real, and at last, at 2:00 a.m. on a Saturday in a fake Art Deco tower in West Hollywood, it was as real as it gets.

For two years, the phones in the better hotels just kept functioning, refused to be the Beefeater throbbing in my ears.

"What's that sound?" my wife asked when she finally caught me in California, the way a traveler might ask about a bump or a rattle. There had been an odd thunk from somewhere deep in my hotel room.

"Hmm, what sound?" I said, the way a flight attendant might pretend that Boeing built it that way. I was looking at a fine woman I didn't know and listening to a beautiful one I did.

"I heard a sound," she said.

"Huh," I slurred. "Well, I certainly wouldn't worry about it."

But here's what they don't tell you. Here's why I really hate unfamiliar airplanes. Those sounds are real. The plane won't always splinter right at that moment, but that engine noise, tuned to the wrong pitch? That thump you hear, that bump or clink or groan? Your instincts are correct. That is absolutely a problem. If you hear that sound again, you should begin to worry, and if you hear it a fifth time, something bad is about to happen, no matter how wide the flight attendant is smiling.

"Who's with you?" she asked. The sound was back. There was no denying it this time: a definite thud in the background. We all heard it. And all at once I saw how this was about to go, was blasé in my jump seat no longer. I looked around and noticed even the veteran travelers starting to freak out, and I began thumping my ring against my tumbler, twirling the rocks and tonic dregs, for once desperate for the lesser sounds of glass and ice.

"It was the bottle, honey. I dropped a bottle. Yes, I'm drinking, and I'm sorry and . . ." And I realized at that exact moment, with a horrifying sensation like the ground coming up at my face, that I needed to say "I'm done." But she beat me to it by two seconds.

"I'm done."

And after that, after she said she was done, I figured for a while that I didn't need to be. It seemed like one done could cover us both. Someone had to continue something.

My life now is charging: whether or not my phone, my laptop, my electric razor is full, and when it can become full again. The thing that really kills me at these junior terminals is the missing outlets. At the moment, I've got my cell phone sucking desperately at the wall, extracting all it can before I take it back into the wild. I'm trying to avoid getting it wet with melting ice. The last thing I can afford is to fry my best charger. The irony is, no one even uses hotel phones anymore.

The outlets are my lifelines—to my boss, to a fresh cheek at a 6:00 p.m. call, to the house that holds my daughter—and all day my head is tied up making calculations about battery drain rate and layover length and how quickly some terminal improvement in Columbus is liable to be proceeding. Everyone knows it's harder to dig yourself out of a rut than to stay out of it in the first place, and part of that for me is all the bad product. But it's also things like the outlets. How are you supposed to get anywhere if you never know where your next charge is coming from, if you're competing with people in first-class lounges operating at full strength?

I got through to my daughter last night, for the first time in weeks. She has a knack for calling just after I've boarded, or finally fallen asleep a time zone east, or mismanaged a call to an unpromising lead and sapped my charge for the afternoon. She thinks she can never reach me, and I hate that that's true, and that I simply don't have the outlets to fix it. There's another man in the stone house now, as there has every right to be. That of all things I can't complain about. I even hope he will be pleasant and stay that way, will know how to snake a toilet and string a ukulele and make a delicious pesto. It will be easier for her that way—a life full of pesto. I could hear him in the background last night, chatting with her mother as they cooked dinner, probably tossing handful after handful of fresh pine nuts into the blender. Plugging that blender into my beautiful surge-protected power strips. Calling for more basil, more Parmesan, more of it all.

She wanted to know when I was going to visit, and I said I did too and she should ask her mother. We both breathed on the line, and I thought about how it's been months since I've been in a terminal as shiny as the one in my old city. I thought about grounded outlets and grounded people, grounded flights and what a marvel it is that the ground used to move for me, right under my feet. Then my phone died.

In a way, the planes make it easier to explain. They're so tragic, so accustomed to taking the heat. They so visibly can't be involved in anything good. She rode along with me once, last summer, on a little 2–2 design you could practically hear Airbus rejecting. She was on her way to camp in the Ozarks, and the Ozarks are the kind of place I ply my trade now. I now work in the regions where my daughter goes to camp. I tried not to watch her eyes as we turned up the aisle. She frowned as I aimed us toward two tiny seats, not budging. "This is us?"

"This is us, honey."

Slowly she took the window. I joined her in the aisle, burying the drinks booklet deep into the seatback pocket. And then suddenly I noticed she was smiling. "Ohhh," she said, looking around at the scuffed walls, the ancient fonts on the emergency instructions. An explanation was finally dawning on her. "So this plane doesn't land in our city."

———

Right now the TV is playing a Canadian Football game, which you get up here in middle Michigan, and I'm lying on top of the comforter, working down a Sierra Mist on ice from the hall machine. I still drink my drinks like they're drinks. It's my one concession to the rhythm of my old addiction. I just got so expert at that first fat slurp, the grimace and sigh. It seems a shame to give something like that up, once you've grown that good at it. I can't afford to throw away the skills I have left. I still lie on top of comforters, too. No self-respecting frequent flier is supposed to even keep it on the bed, but I figure with where I am now, a few jiggers of bacteria aren't going to change my situation appreciably. Anyway, who said I was a self-respecting flier?

I went down to the lobby a little while ago, for the Wi-Fi connection. I deliberately send emails at 9:00 p.m. now, always bcc'ing my boss. I spike them with attentive details about the time and place, lace them with invitations to breakfast meetings. Then I check them over three times, petrified of typos. I worry I am one "teh," one late-night "adn" away from another downgrade in product, and the next level fits in no roller suitcase. One lucky thing about these terrible hotels is that they usually don't have bars, or thick walls, but this one has both. And I needed to prime some leads. I needed to get them wondering about the bag.

So I plodded downstairs, quickly tethering myself to the charging station near the front desk. I started out well, just focused on putting one letter in front of another. I referenced the brand of bath products carried in my own hotel's shower. I found an excuse to add some specifics about the Continental spread. What praise I lavished on these woody croissants. But after about fifteen minutes, my eyes started to drift over to the little bar. It's really more of a *barrette*, tucked behind the elevators, but even the flimsiest hotel pub is a wonder of diversity. It's something you crave when you're exiled to the suburbia of teetotaling. All those liqueurs, in their emerald and sapphire bottles, from all those nations. It's a kind of traveling itself.

There was a single drinker there, throwing himself at a chalice of something beige. Every thirty seconds or so he would tilt his head back and crunch a mouthful of ice. The sound cracked around the bare lobby. I could forgive the color of the drink, I thought. But there is no noise like teeth on wet bar ice. I loathe it. That ice has been put there to cool your spirit, a noble purpose. You have been supplied peanuts to crunch. Leave the ice to its work.

Really, if he'd just been drinking a better drink better, I would have been fine. I would have put my head down and dug back into the wonders of spellcheck. But he was drinking like a hack. I made eye contact with the bartender. I rolled my eyes, and she rolled them back, and that hadn't happened in a while. And before I knew what I was doing, I was rising from my seat to call for Bombay and demonstrate to him how it was done.

Thank God for this rotten company laptop. This old warhorse I have cursed so many times. Made of obsolete metals. Too wide for the tray table in an exit row, not graced with a magnetic plug to disengage if your foot kicks the cord. I took two steps toward the bar—and the blessed thing laid me flat on the linoleum.

I looked up to see the front desk clerk and the bartender gazing down at me. The White Russian and its drinker had disappeared. The laptop was wobbling up and down at the edge of the desk, nodding contentedly in my direction.

"OK, no more for *you*," the bartender said with a wink. She helped me up with soft hands.

As soon as I got back upstairs, I staggered into the bathroom and swept all the conditioners off the vanity, stuffing them into the fridge. Then I spilled a gush of soda into this glass. I propped myself up on the bed and forced myself to slow down. And I began sipping it the old way, the way it was meant to be sipped. And even though nothing but sugar was flowing, I started to feel better. I started to feel like myself again. When my wife said she was done, and I wasn't ready to be done, what I really wasn't ready to give up was being an expert at something. It's just like the airplanes. You can keep your leather seats, your acres of legroom. I don't miss the luxury. I miss the mastery.

———

It's getting late now. It's my last night at this hotel. I've retrieved a new pack of ice from down the hall and am pressing it against my face. Tomorrow I take my next hop-skip, a connector from here in Kalamazoo down to Kentucky, via somewhere somewhat in between. As with too many trips lately, my sales on this jaunt have not gone well. I've got only the morning to make back the cost of the flights, and so far my lead in Battle Creek hasn't let me open the case. I can't even get them to muse on what's inside. The truth is, even I sometimes forget. I'll be eight slides in and it will occur to me: I have zero memory of what I'm selling. And this helps. It's useful that I can't remember. Good for my soul and good for my sell. My pitch now is based on curiosity alone—the fact that when you don't know what's in a bag, you want someone to open it. And when I can't recall, I can channel my own curiosity. "Hmm, wonder what's in *here* . . ." They can't imagine I'm being sincere. "Feel it," I say. "*Heavy*." They are duly impressed. I carry it around all day. Who would do that if it weren't something good? Who could respect himself? Finally, I drop the punch line: "And it doesn't even fit in the overhead."

I am pitching them on my own pain, and it is moderately effective. Just enough to make the pain sustainable. But the limitations are obvious. The sheer weight of a bag can only take you so far. This afternoon I watched them glaze over as I gave my pitch, sipping on coffee that wasn't there. Believe me, I wanted to tell them: I know what a sip is and what a sip isn't. "How's the coffee?" I asked. "What if I told you that what's in this case is *better than coffee*?" They didn't wonder what then. I massaged my aching shoulders where the strap digs in. They didn't ask what was wrong. This is my test of their attention. The bag rolls. So I pretended I was having a problem with my PowerPoint and cut the thing short. I can't afford to spend my material when there's no chance, to use myself up. I can only beg for curiosity so many times before I get fed up and spill the beans. I still long to make the elegant promises I used to, with my old product. I can't offer them that easiest thing of all to sell, so much more marketable than a worse version of me, which is a better version of them.

So tomorrow morning I get to start again, from the beginning. To struggle my way back into that room, scan my surroundings for other things my bag could be. Maybe the bruise from my fall will help. Pulling away the ice pack, I can see that it's already starting to turn an interesting purple. It could give me a whole new story.

My hopes may not be what you'd call sky-high. But then I will walk out of that room, and I will get a second chance. Because then it's back to the airport. And once I get back to the airport, there is always a possibility. Because some days, I'll slouch into the terminal, thinking about nothing more than what dinner foods I'll be eating for breakfast, what sorry yogurt I'll be packing up for dinner. I'll gaze doubtfully up at the board, already taking my clothes off for security, not bothering to remove my belt, because I no longer bother to wear one. And then I'll notice that it's a proper gate listed up there. Vitamin gates, we used to call them: B6, B12, C. And I'll suddenly find out that my puddle jumper has been replaced by a sleek 757, a sturdy A320—even, every once in a great while, a big, beaming 767, like the kind I used to take. Forget the Bs, this one is flying out of A1: steak sauce, we used to call it. They'll have tacked a leg onto the beginning of a transatlantic flight, and I'll have the sublime experience of flying from, say, Charlotte to Philadelphia on a grand double-aisle. I will share in the beginning of some plane's long trip. I'll briefly be a part of something big. Entire families will be around me, not split up, in fact barely making a dent in their row. And somehow that will be all it takes to pull me back. As I stride out of the airport and hail a car to my client, I'll get a glint in my eye that even I can see. And on those days I know I'll be leaving my heavy bag behind.

About the Author

THEO SCHELL-LAMBERT is a writer based in New Orleans. His work has appeared in McSweeney's *Internet Tendency*, the *Village Voice*, the *Believer*, and the *San Francisco Chronicle*, among other publications. His debut novel will be published by Little A in the spring.

Theo on Writing
Small Bottles

John McPhee. McPhee is my favorite *New Yorker* writer. He handles hard data and technical information in a way that makes them fascinating. (Making anything fascinating is kind of a mandate of the *New Yorker*, but it's McPhee who takes it to hard geology and transportation systems.) Why are rocks boring in someone else's hands, but not McPhee's? The best I can figure is that (1) he pretends they're not boring, and (2) he writes about them with a kind of language of love. Be specific enough about anything, and art will be revealed. When I had the protagonist dig into his obsession with different airplane configurations, I was thinking about McPhee.

The McDonnell Douglas MD-80. This story started with its first two sentences, which came to me on a flight between Denver and Santa Ana. The plane I was sitting on was similar to the current standard-issue 737s and Airbus 319s, except it had only two seats on one side, which I believe was more common in the previous generation of midsize airliners. The card said it was an MD-80. Well, so what? Modern airline travel is pitched as this kind of identical experience—you're supposed to have the same trip every time, and in some sense you usually do. But it struck me that there's also this other layer of the story, in which every plane is different, and the little differences between aircraft matter. Essentially my thought was flights are predicated on travelers tuning out the details, and what if a frequent traveler became completely tuned into them? What if someone paid attention?

***The Emigrants* by W. G. Sebald.** This is probably the least trackable influence on this list, but reading Sebald has strongly affected the way I think about characters in the context of their little historical moment. This story is in large part about time, about humans and technology both aging at slightly different paces, about feeling detached from the modern world while living amid its hardest quotidian details. We are now owned by the random arrangement of the outlets in the airport terminal. Who even picked where they'd be placed? Sebald is also, like Nabokov, great at writing about people in motion: on trains, on rambles, on pilgrimages.

Mary Karr and Rosie Schaap. Writing about drinking is tricky. Its cool and its banality both need to be acknowledged. Drinking one martini at a hotel bar is one thing; drinking two gins at a motel minibar another. For me, the poet and memoirist Mary Karr is a writer who's managed to capture both the élan and clumsiness of booze. Rosie Schaap, the drink columnist for the *New York Times Magazine*, also writes terrifically about drinking culture and what of it has merit—the camaraderie in bars is genuinely noble, I think—and what is ugly. I wanted to make sure my protagonist missed some genuinely good things about something that was inarguably bad—that he'd lost something valid, too. That tension interested me.

Hats **by the Blue Nile, and** *Paracosm* **by Washed Out.** A lot of writers write about how they can't write to music, especially music with words. I don't feel that way. (I do a lot of writing in coffee shops, and I think the process of actively tuning out words—while absorbing a tone—is productive for me.) But I do need to listen to the same one or two albums for the entirety of a piece: no switching once I'm in. I wrote the first draft of this story while listening to Scottish band the Blue Nile; their atmospherics felt suited to airplanes and airports. I revised it while playing *Paracosm* to death—another atmospheric, spacious album, but with the emotions a bit closer to the surface, which is usually what you want out of a revision.

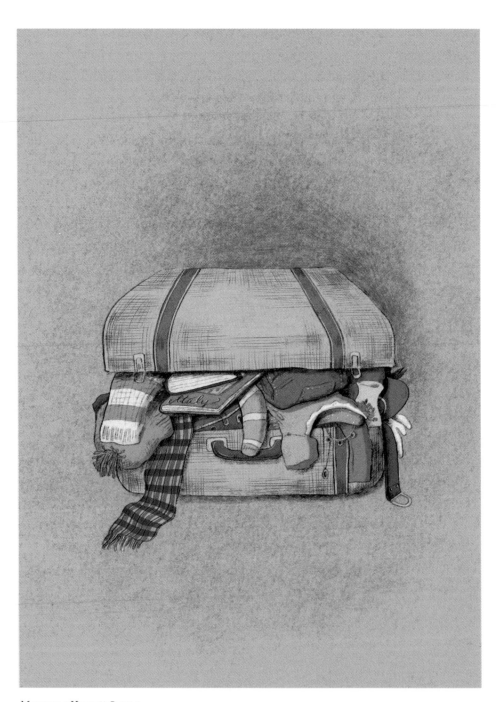

Maryanna Hoggatt © 2014

LA SEPOLTURA

KHALIAH WILLIAMS

It's past three in the morning and, save the bakers just starting to push around newly made dough on their worktables, and the tourists spilling out of nightclubs holding the hands of locals—drunk, sweaty, and hazy in love, the city's working population is sleeping. I am awake, standing in my kitchen, shivering from the winter draft that has crept into the apartment. I stirred from my sleep because our phone is ringing. When I answer, I find my mother on the other end of the line. She tells me that my father is dead, and asks if I could please do the right thing and come home. And though I hardly knew him, I agree to board a plane and return to the United States. I am twenty-four years old, living in Florence, Italy, and no more fatherless than I was when I went to bed four hours before.

In the morning, Nini, my husband, asks who called in the middle of the night. "Tua mamma?"

"Yes," I tell him. "My father is dead. I need to go back to the United States."

"Ma non lo conoscevi." *You didn't even know him*, he reminds me. He is calculating the cost of a last-minute ticket to the States.

"I need to go. My mother has asked me."

"Tesoro, non posso—"

"Don't worry. I know you're busy. I should go alone anyway. You'll come home with me another time," I tell him. It's a lie, but it's the polite thing to say, and if we are anything to each other, we are polite. I pull the largest suitcase we own from the hall closet and pack for Philadelphia in February.

Just before we were married, I explained to Nini (as best I could) that my father had left when I was five. This was not what Nini wanted to hear at the beginning of our affair, spent mostly in bed. He was interested in a different kind of America. Not the one where men leave behind their children and wives. He wanted stories about my childish impulses and teenage brushes with love.

"If we're naked in bed tangled in the sheets," he said, "tell a story that doesn't kill the mood." So I told him about when I slept with my high school English teacher when I was eighteen. Just the month before, the teacher had handed me an essay with my first C and told me that I had to earn the A. I told Nini that I left for college at the end of the summer brokenhearted, because the teacher had decided to marry his long-suffering girlfriend.

"What happened to the man who gave up such a treasure?" Nini wanted to know, smiling greedily at the scandalous nature of it all. Then he laughed with the same kind of wickedness that had drawn me to him at the beginning, when I told him that my teacher's girlfriend eventually left him and that when he called me soon after, I ignored the ringing phone for days.

"But you loved him, no?"

"Ero affogato." *I was drowning in love.*

"And what about now, with me?" he wants to know.

"Sto ancora affogando," I'd told him. *I'm still drowning.*

But now I know how to hold my breath long enough to survive.

"Regina, tesoro, quando torni?" Nini asks when he sees that I have emptied our closet of my clothing, that the dresser drawers are bare.

I shrug and say I'll come back after the funeral. I pack everything. There is surprisingly little that I call my own. He drives me to the airport just before his afternoon classes. During the ride, he looks at me with nervous glances, and I wonder what questions he wants to ask.

When we arrive at the airport, he puts a hand on my knee. "I would wait with you, but—"

"Giotto's crosses," I say. "I know. I'll be fine."

———

The customs officer in Philadelphia, a tall, lanky woman with skin the color of brown ocher, smooths down imaginary flyaway hairs from her tightly pulled bun before taking the passport from my hands. She examines the cover of the well-worn document before opening its pages, speckled with coffee stains and flecks of dried Chianti. It looks more like a coaster than a federal document.

When my Italian citizenship came through last year, I treated my American identity with less care, but now it provides convenience, a bit of comfort. It gives me a name that makes sense in America, Regina Henry. My Italian passport calls me by another name, Regina Casadei. The officer turns to the last pages, thumbing through my expired student visa to the final stamp.

"You've been gone a long time," she says, raising an accusatory eyebrow. "What brings you back?"

"My father died," I say.

She nods, and I can tell she wants to say more, to offer a word or two of sympathy. Instead, she gives me a second nod that says she won't ask any more questions. She flattens my passport to an empty page and brings her stamp down, marking the date and granting me entry back into the country I had given up without hesitation. She returns the small book to my waiting hands, and as I walk away, she gives me a line she delivers a hundred times a day: "Welcome home."

My mother had to circle the airport while I cleared customs. She doesn't get out of the car to greet me or help with the enormous suitcase I struggle to shove into the backseat. When I get in the car, her teeth are clenched in frustration, but she relaxes a little when I lock the seat belt in place. She takes me in as though she expected someone different.

"Looks like you've lost weight," she says, and then she reaches out and touches my hair, which I keep cut close to my head. "I can't believe you walk around like this." She grabs and releases a handful of knots and curls, as if she finds them offensive.

"It's easier this way," I tell her. "Besides, the only person I know who does hair in Florence is this Senegalese woman and, I swear, the last time I let her perm it, she nearly took out all my hair. Maybe I'll do something different while I'm in Philly. I bet it's cheaper here. Anyway, I suppose I could use a change."

She asks why Nini didn't come with me. I explain that he is teaching four classes this semester on top of tutoring. He's also working on an article about Renaissance art, about Giotto's crosses. I say he's sorry he couldn't come, that he really wants to meet her. But buying one ticket at the last minute was expensive enough.

An airport cop taps the hood of my mother's car, an old blue Camry she's had since I was in high school. We've lingered too long. She shifts the gear into drive, and we pull away from the airport.

In the rearview mirror I watch friends and family greet one another with the kind of warmth my mother reserves for strangers. She wasn't always this way. I'd often hear my grandmother say to anyone who would listen, "That boy took my happy child and left me this sad one."

"Well, at least he still has a teaching job, after what you two pulled." A few short minutes into our reunion and we are back in familiar territory.

"They don't fire you for marrying a student, Mother. The Italians are more progressive about things like that. They're not as puritanical as Americans."

This is not exactly true. It *had* been a minor scandal when I moved into Nini's flat on Via dei Neri two weeks after the program ended and the other girls had either returned to America or left for vacations in Greece or Paris. There had been threats of termination, but then, to everyone's surprise, Nini proposed, and there was nothing left to question. When I told Anna Rita, my Florentine host mother, of my intention to stay and marry, as she had so often suggested during the year I lived in her spare bedroom, she offered the only advice she thought I needed. She gave a slight tug at the lower lid of her right eye with the pad of her index finger and said, "Stai attenta, cara—è Sienese. Sono furbi." *Watch out, dear—he's from Siena. They're cunning.*

"I don't understand why I had to come back for this," I say, looking out at the scenery of Route 76, as if I'd had no part in the decision.

"Reggie," my mother says, softening her tone. She's the only one who calls me Reggie, to everyone else I'm Regina, la signora Casadei, or, worse, among Nini's university friends, la fanciulla americana, *the American girl.*

"So what am I supposed to do?" I say. "Who's going to be there?"

"I suppose his family. His mother—your other grandmother. He knew a lot of people, and it's not like he ever forgot his friends. He always did have a lot of friends."

"They don't want me to say anything, do they? I don't have anything to say. I barely remember him."

"All you have to do is go. Make some peace." She doesn't say anything else for a long time.

I keep looking at her expectantly, and her grip on the steering wheel tightens.

"Are you happy there? With him?" She doesn't take her eyes off the road.

"Being in a marriage is hard, of course, but it's fine," I say. A year ago I might have said yes. But her question has come too late.

"We're both so busy these days," I continue. "The article he's writing, I keep track of his notes. And then I work a few nights in a bar and take classes at the university. I'm finishing my degree. There's not much time for anything else."

There is nothing else to tell but the stresses, the struggles over money, my never-ending search for employment, the inconsistency with which I contribute to the household, my part-time work in student bars where I had once been a frequent customer. I could tell her about the girls I hear about, new students from places like Oklahoma or Kansas or wherever girls like that come from, the ones who are just a few years younger but new enough that they're still enchanted by the accent, girls who still sound out their newly acquired language, substituting the swollen Italian vowels and consonants for flat English ones. I could tell her about the baby I thought I didn't want but still took offense at when it rejected me. These are the things my mother has been waiting to hear.

"How long you planning to stay?"

"The ticket's open-ended. Maybe a week. Maybe two."

"That's a big bag for a week, maybe two."

"Is it? We don't travel much anymore. It's very expensive in Florence now."

The remains of a snowstorm have left a thin, slushy film of gray on the Philadelphia streets, and I remember that I have left my boots behind. This time of year Florence is cold, and the air is so damp that the chill penetrates all the way to my bones. No matter how many layers I put on, I'm always cold in the winter, always sick. Nini says it's because I'm not Italian, because I wasn't born to breathe their oxygen for longer than a vacation. He likes to say it will take a lifetime before my lungs and body get used to the air there. But after four winters of trying and not trying, I know that a lifetime is no longer something I am willing to give.

"Your grandmother will be happy to see you," my mother says, breaking the silence. "She's moving a little slower, but her mind is still sharp. She's in your old room, so I put you in the spare room. There's not much in there, but I can move a TV in if you want."

"Don't worry about it, Mommy. I'll be fine."

She takes her hand from the steering wheel and gives my knee a slight squeeze. "Mommy" gets her every time.

She turns off at the exit for City Avenue and then again onto Lincoln Drive. We slowly follow the winding road that leads us into Germantown, just barely keeping up with the pace of traffic. My body moves along with the car as it takes curve after curve. I haven't forgotten what it's like to be on these roads, and for a second I feel like I'm home.

"It's good to have you here, Reggie." My mother takes her eyes off the road for a moment and looks at me. "I couldn't do this without you."

———

My swollen belly had been unexpected but welcome. I'd thought that it might be the event that would bring my mother back into my life, and it would confirm that I was not just a passing phase for Nini.

The night I woke up to sharp pains and a warm wetness running down my leg, Nini wasn't home. Anna Rita arrived at the same time as the medics and came along with me in the ambulance, where I lost consciousness, and the life inside of me. In the hospital, after Nini arrived with excuses for his absence, they told us it had been a boy. Nini reached for my hand as he began to weep for something I hadn't known he wanted, but I pulled away from him, feeling he deserved to go through this as alone as I had.

When I came home from the hospital, Nini asked if he should call my mother, ask her to come. "E perché?" I'd snapped. There would have been nothing to say. I hadn't yet told her I was pregnant. For four long months I'd kept the secret, waiting for the right moment. So there was no reason to tell her that something had been lost. I retreated to our bedroom and locked the door, wondering if the miscarriage was a punishment. Nini took up residence in the small living room of our flat, knocking at the bedroom door two or three times a day and receiving no response.

When I eventually emerged, we started living in silence, moving through the five rooms of our home while trying to avoid each other, speaking only when necessary, about bills and schedules—conversations that often started quietly but ended in screams and tears. Two months later, when my shape had nearly returned, I got my mother's call in the middle of the night.

Now, here in the house I grew up in, my school portraits line the walls next to photos of deceased relatives, events I have missed taking part in, and reproductions of paintings my mother loves. The living room looks cluttered, so different from the minimalist aesthetic Nini insists on. The walls of our apartment are mostly bare, even though he spends hours in churches across Italy studying the country's history through art.

I set my suitcase by the door and look around as if I'm new to this place. My grandmother is sitting in front of the television in a recliner, the sound of her snores rising above the episode of *Murder, She Wrote* she was watching. She wakes immediately when the door closes and my mother slides the locks into place.

"Well, well. It's been a minute or two since I last set eyes on you." Nan opens her arms wide, "Come here and give this old lady some sugar."

I cross the room quickly and find myself in her small, thin arms. She's frail, frailer than I remember her being, but that's what time does to us. She releases me and leans back into the chair. Then she beckons me forward and takes my face in her hands, which are dry and cracked from the winter air.

She pulls my face closer to hers, like she wants to inspect me.

"Well, don't you look the same! I thought you'd come back looking, I don't know, more Eye—" She looks over at my mother. "*E*-talian." She stresses the *e* like she's been practicing.

"Nan, it's not like I was on another planet. The only difference is the language. And the wine. They drink a lot of wine."

She picks up the remote control and lifts it over my head to turn down the volume. "They got an Italian version of Jessica Fletcher over there? They should!"

"I think so, Nan—I missed you so much." I grab her into another hug, and she laughs.

"Of course you did. Your own fault too. Running around the world like the white girls do. I told your mother—"

"Nan, I brought you a couple of gifts."

Her eyes light up, and I know she's forgotten one of her favorite topics of conversation. In the days before I'd left for Italy the first time around, she'd talked about my going away with a mixture of pride and apprehension. The world she knew was still very black and white, and though she was excited for me, Europe was definitely white.

"Good. Good. Then you can tell me all about Italy." She pronounces "Italy" as if the *a* is silent. "And Nino."

"Nini," I remind her.

She lifts the remote control high in the air again and turns the volume back up. "What's for dinner?" Nan says.

My mother gives her a look as she hangs her coat in the closet by the front door.

I walk over to my suitcase, and with all my strength, I start to make my way up the stairs. "Just let me get unpacked and I'll help."

"You not tired?" my mother asks me. She's already lying down on the couch. Her eyes are closed.

"I slept on the plane."

"Nino, Nini, Ninny. Whatever floats your boat," I hear Nan mutter under her breath.

"What kind of name is Nini?" my mother had asked in the first phone conversation after I got married.

I told her it was a nickname, though I agreed that maybe he should have long ago settled on something more appropriate for a man his age. Gio, Vanni, or Gianni would all be better, but at nearly forty years old, he's still called by his baby name, and it fits.

At our wedding, his sister told me that I'd made a fine choice. "Brava," she'd said. "You've chosen an Italian man who could put all others to shame with the way he chases women. You'll have to be the one to adapt. He never will."

I laughed nervously, as if she'd told an inappropriate joke. Besides, I thought, what could change a man more than marriage.

For the better part of a year, I was right, and then again, when I was first pregnant. He would come home every night, prepare meals, cater to my needs and wants. He used to go down a list of names for the baby, always boy names: Gianluca, Pietro, Alessio. But eventually he fell back into comfortable behaviors, leaving me home alone more often than not.

———

From the spare room, I hear the phone ring. A few moments later, my mother calls my name. When I come down to the living room, she is holding the handset out to me.

"It's your husband," she says with a look of skepticism, as if until this moment she had doubted his existence. I hesitate, but I take the phone.

"Pronto. Regina?"

"Pronto. I just got in. I would have called."

"Pensavo . . . beh . . . e comé? Come ti senti?" *I was thinking . . . well . . . how is it? How do you feel?*

"It's fine. I don't know. It's been a while," I speak to him in Italian because I feel my mother and grandmother's eyes watching my uneasiness with a man I'm supposed to be comfortable with. The less they understand, the better.

"La sepoltura?"

"The burial? It's tomorrow. Listen, I'm tired. It was a long flight. I'll call later."

"We'll talk when you come back? There are things we should talk about."

"I know. But now, well, now is not the time. When I get back."

"Ti voglio bene, tesoro."

"Ti voglio bene."

I intend to unpack, but there's no dresser in the spare room. I empty the contents of my suitcase onto the bed and look at the pathetic jumble of books, clothing, and trinkets I've brought with me. My entire world in one bag and there isn't much of value to it. I shove everything onto the floor and stretch out on the bed. A catnap. A quiet moment to assess the state of affairs that have brought me all the way back to Philadelphia. I tell myself I'm not tired, but when I hear my mother call my name, two hours have passed and dinner is ready.

Over the dinner she cooked while I was asleep, she says it was a heart attack. That he'd been ill for a long time. She says that he called for me a few months ago, looking to make amends for the life he'd given up with us. She told him I was gone and reminded him that he had no right to me even if I had been there. She didn't know he was sick when he called. I ask her if it would have changed things.

"I don't think so, Reggie. A few months ago I wasn't ready to stop being angry. Now he's not here. What's the sense in being angry at a memory?"

I don't disagree with her.

"Is that why you asked me to come back?"

"I thought it was time we get stuff straightened out between us. Between all of us. I know you don't have the same memories I have, but I guess I want you to make peace with whatever memories you do have inside that head of yours." She starts to clear the table and walks over to the sink. I sit there wondering if it's even possible to make things right.

"I had to cross an ocean to do that? What if I already made peace? What if I stopped being angry at him a long time ago?"

"Well then, sometimes a mother just needs her child. One day you'll understand that."

Here is the moment I've spent six months waiting for, when I could explain to my mother that I finally understood the bond between mother and child, and that now I know what my leaving had done to her—broken her just a little bit, made her feel empty. I want to tell her that I understand that emptiness, to tell her that I, too, have felt the strangely happy burden of carrying life inside of me only to one day have nothing to show for it. I think about opening my mouth and telling her about the baby and the infidelities and the silence. I want to say that I longed to have her get on a plane just to rub my back and tell me that things would never be the same but they might be okay one day.

"And what about us?" I say.

She puts the dishes she has been holding in the sink and turns to me, water dripping from the tips of her fingers, landing silently on the floor.

"I had so many plans for you, Reggie, and you threw it all away. And for what? So you could marry some man nearly twice your age and work in a bar? That place won't ever be your home. I don't care how hard you pretend you aren't from here."

"This isn't my fault. It's not my fault he left you—us. What happened with me is different. I fell in love with someone and started a new life." I get up from my chair and walk the small distance to the kitchen door. "I did it for me. I never shut you out, but you were just so angry. You were always welcome in our home."

"Now? Am I still welcome?"

"You're always welcome wherever I am. Just like this will always be *my* home, right?"

She nods and turns back to the sink, and as I walk out of the room, I hear nothing but the running water and the clanging of metal pots against ceramic dishes. But underneath it all, I know she is humming.

———

In the morning we drink coffee and eat dry toast and hard-boiled eggs with my grandmother before getting back in the car and driving clear across the city for the funeral. I am wearing the only black dress I own, a flimsy piece of silk fabric that I wear when I need to show up somewhere and be the wife of a professor. In it I feel even less like a daughter in mourning and more like a vagabond, dusty and rank from the weariness of travel.

The church is little more than a storefront, nothing like the ancient cathedrals and basilicas of Florence. I start to pull the door open, but my mother grabs my shoulder.

"Wait," she says. She is breathing heavily, and she puts her hand over her heart as she exhales. "I think I need a cigarette. Something to calm my nerves."

I reach into my shoulder bag and pull out the smashed pack of cigarettes that has been languishing at the bottom of the bag for who knows how long. She raises an eyebrow and takes one.

"Since when do you smoke?"

"Everyone smokes." I reach back in and fish for a lighter. I come up with one of Nini's, a sleek Zippo I bought him on vacation in Amsterdam.

My mother takes a cigarette, and I hold out the lighter, which she also accepts. "I quit, you know. This is my first one in months."

"Are you alright? Do you want me to go find you some water or something?" She shakes her head and lights the cigarette before returning the lighter to my care. I light one for myself. "I quit too. I mean, I stopped smoking. I don't even remember buying this pack."

She looks at me and exhales a cloud of smoke. "I should say so. You don't have any business smoking."

"I stopped smoking when I found out I was pregnant."

"Reggie—"

"I had a miscarriage. They don't know why. I mean, they couldn't find a reason."

"You should have called me. I would have come to you. I would have." She tosses the cigarette into the street. "You should have said something."

"I kept waiting and waiting for the right time to tell you I was pregnant, and then it was too late. It was all over, and I was all by myself. I wanted you there, but I didn't know what to say. And then I didn't have the words for it." Now the words fall from my lips, quickly and freely.

I try to take a drag from my cigarette, but my hand is shaking. I need something to steady me. My mother reaches for me, and I let the cigarette fall to the ground. She takes my cold, shaking hands into her warm, steady ones.

"It's okay," she says. I nod and try not to cry. An older man opens the church door and tells us the service is about to start. With my free hand, I pull my coat tightly around my body and follow my mother inside.

There are no more than ten mourners, the two of us included. I don't recognize anyone by name or sight, but I figure they must be the relatives who were lost to me many years ago when my father packed up the back of his car and drove away.

I remember the day well. I helped him carry his suitcase, an old thrift-store treasure he and my mother had bought in Old City the first time he went on tour. It wasn't until later I realized that everything he owned, every instrument, was in the trunk of the car. He didn't say when he would be back. When he closed the trunk, my mother went inside and shut the screen door real hard. He pulled one of my ponytails and kissed me on the cheek.

"I'm gonna go make some noise," he said. That's what he always said when he practiced or when he had a gig. "I'm gonna go make some noise." I saw him once or twice after that, but after a couple of years he was just gone.

In the funeral program, I'm not mentioned as surviving the deceased. Neither is my mother. We sit in the back of the church, and from the distance I can see the outline of my father's face, his profile, but no specific features. My mother asks if I would like to see him before they close the casket, and I shake my head. I've come as far as I can. I'd buried the idea of my father long ago, and even if I want to be angry at being expected to repeat the task, to do it all over again, I can't. I know why I am here: this is a moment for my mother; it is her peace that is being made here today, and it is my job to sit beside her as she does it.

She rises from the metal folding chair next to mine and processes down the aisle toward the open coffin. In her right hand, she clutches a small familiar black bag, where she has kept her wedding band. Never divorced, my mother is finally the widow she has claimed to be all these years. At the gray-and-silver casket, she leans over the body of the man she must have once loved the way I once loved Nini, and she whispers something. She lingers there for just a moment before turning around and coming back to me. She makes eye contact with people she once called family. She nods at them and then sits back down.

She takes my hand and speaks to me in a whisper. "I'm not saying you should come back here or stay over there. That's up to you. But you have a history there now, and it's complicated with a marriage and death, and I know I've been saying different, but those are strong ties. They don't break so easily."

The preacher, a willowy man with a long face covered in wrinkles and lines that suggest he is well into his seventh decade, gives the eulogy. They knew each other well, my father and this man. His eyes are wet with tears, and his voice is gravelly with emotion. He speaks of my father the musician and says the way he played the piano was a thing of beauty. He says my father played the trumpet with such heart that after two notes, you knew exactly who was blowing into that horn even if you couldn't see him. His instruments, he says, were like his children, well cared for and nourished by his passion for the melodies he played. He is crying now, sobbing for a man I can't really remember and didn't ever really know.

He starts to leave the podium but then comes back. "Marty," he says, "didn't always know how to do the right thing. Sometimes he didn't even try to do the right thing. But when he did, you could see he had a good soul, a good heart. It was in his music. He made a lot of people happy making that noise."

My mother squeezes my hand, because she knows I can't remember a single note he ever played.

———

After the doctors informed Nini and me of our loss, I went to sleep and let Nini handle everything. If there was a baptism, I know nothing about it. If there was a service of some kind, I did not attend. The details I had cared about were tiny clothes and shoes, bassinets and strollers, stockpiled in Nini's office, which was soon to be converted into a nursery. It was all gone by the time I was wheeled from the hospital and taken home in a taxi with an armful of sympathy cards and flowers.

When my father's service is over, we get back in the car and drive in the silence I am so familiar with. My mother looks straight ahead, focused on the road in front of us. I watch the sidewalks, see mothers tugging their small ones, bundled up so tight that their little limbs can do nothing but remain outstretched. I feel the longing that has not left me in these last few months. If I could, I would trick myself into going back, into staying and making a home with my husband.

Once, my mother told me that she had no more tears to give my father. I wonder if I will ever feel the same about Nini, about the baby. I think about the kind of father my husband would have been. Would he have stayed Nini, the boy, or grown into Giovanni, the man? I wonder if I would have been a good mother or if my youthful impulses would have overshadowed my maternal instincts. I wish I could tell my mother that I will stay with her, that I am ready to come back, but I know that leaving an unfinished life with Nini would be no better than the way my father left us behind.

About the Author

Originally from Philadelphia, **KHALIAH WILLIAMS** resides in Baltimore, where she works as a college counselor and English teacher. She is a graduate of Sarah Lawrence College and received an MFA in fiction writing from the Iowa Writers' Workshop. In 2013 she was selected as a Kimbilio Fellow. Currently she's working on a novel and a collection of short stories.

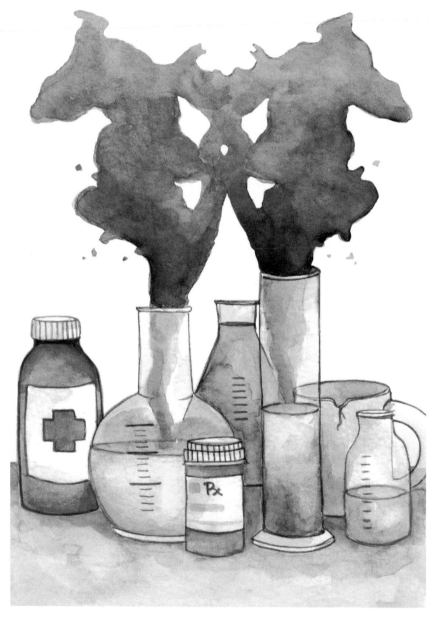

Brooke Weeber © 2014

THE INAUDIBLE FREQUENCY OF LONGING

KIRBY ALLEN

Lab Report #6160891

Title:

The Manifestation of Abstract Affection Properties in Small Mammals and the Detrimental Physical Effects Thereof

Lab Partners:

Me
You (in absentia)

Materials:

The Rat Room under the stairs, Woods Laboratory
2 lab rats, adult and infant
Inadequate sleep
Full moon
Orange mohair cardigan
Tortoiseshell reading glasses
7.5 cups of coffee
2 chipped beige industrial-grade coffee mugs

Blue oxford button-down, still smelling of you
12,495.5 km, the distance between us
86 days
Negative space you left behind
2 letters, unaddressed, postage incalculable
Epstein-Barr virus, untreated for approx. 6 wks
300 ml tequila
3.79 liters Cactus Libre margarita mix
1.77 grams marijuana ("Super Diesel")
30 mg hydrocodone cough syrup
1 1988 Volvo station wagon, peak speed before impact 17.7 km/hr.
Live oak tree, approx. 200 years old
Emergency room, St. Benedict Memorial

1 pair seafoam-green nonskid socks
Whale-print pajama pants, drawstring removed
2 antiseptic blue hospital gowns
Bleach-scented cotton waffle blanket
20 mg haloperidol
2 mg lorazepam
150 mg bupropion
72 meters of horseshoe-shaped hallway
4 trees (indeterminate deciduous) behind glass
The purple crayon I'm now using to record data

Purpose

Statement of the problem:

There are several.

1. How can something invisible, insubstantial, and therefore unquantifiable affect the physiology of a biological entity?

(Subjects studied: common brown rats [*Rattus norvegicus*] and their captors [*Homo sapiens*].)

2. Property derivation is clear; it is the precipitate of close contact between two (or, theoretically, more) subjects. But it is unclear how this intangible property is affected by physical factors such as time and space.

3. If this property is imaginary, how can it manifest physical change in the subject(s) exposed?

4. What is the nature of said property (elastic or inelastic), which seems impossible to dissolve or forcibly sever, even over distance (approximately 12,495.5 km) and time (as yet to be determined).

5. You left without saying good-bye.

6. Once one has been committed to the care of a psychiatric facility, he or she is no longer entitled to caffeinated coffee, closed doors, sharp corners, decisions.

Preliminary Observations

You have a better facility for academic jargon, structure, rules. If you were to read this, you would read it with a red pen. But I have a better memory, a fact even you conceded once, and this is how it happened:

You wore an orange sweater under your lab coat the night I met you, two in the morning, bleary-eyed under fluorescent lab lights. Your research project escaped after consuming four of its five offspring. You were three floors and a wing away from your own lab, down in the wood-paneled basement. My department—dingy, forgotten Entomology. I left my moths to help you. We searched the avocado halls, tiptoeing, but our sneakers still squeaked louder than scrabbling rodents.

"No shoes," you said, quieter than mice. Sock-footed, we found her almost an hour later on top of the upstairs lounge microwave, halfway through her third package of peanut-butter crackers.

"How is she still hungry?"

"It's not," you said and took her by the scruff like a kitten.

I followed you to a wooden door, unmarked, under the back stairs. I'd passed it three or four times a day for years and assumed it was a broom closet. The Rat Room. Inside, under a sloping ceiling: stacks of wire cages, rat piss and cedar shavings, two hundred black-glass eyes tracking our movements. We went through them like sheets of paper. You reached into the cage and pulled out the last baby rat, a newspaper shred clinging to its naked pink skin. I held out my cupped hands, and you indifferently dropped the rat in, like a licorice jelly bean.

"What happens now?" I asked.

This time you fastened the mother's cage door with a padlock.

Hypothesis

[love]: a qualification for this abstract property, which is neither solid, liquid, or gas, but is possibly a sublimation of the body and the yawning nothingness that exists between molecules of matter—a telegraph that very nearly spans the infinite distance between two minds. And though the mind is part of the brain/body/meat, it does not seem to be wholly corporeal; it is the same with this nonmaterial property, tethering one subject to another. And though the tether has no physical presence, if severed, aftereffects are felt in the physical realm, creating a sensation not unlike being hollowed like a melon with a plastic cafeteria spork. Insides scraped pithless, cavernous, a near-complete nothingness, smelling of ozone. What seeps in after is drowsy-making, heavier than tungsten and just as inert, but somehow simultaneously alive and seething, acidic, slowly chewing its way to the outside.

The sudden onset of tether-severance—for instance, when one unsuspecting subject receives a message reading *Moved to Abu Dhabi, Thought you should know*—may catalyze an uncharacteristically melodramatic, but wholly physical, series of ever-worsening events, which could, hypothetically, result in an involuntary (and completely unnecessary!) observational confinement for a minimum of seventy-two hours.

Procedure

Burns, the blonde nurse with tyrannosaurus arms, finds me in the day-room.

"Leave your crayons," she says, but I fold up the construction paper and take it with me. At the nurses' station there's a familiar-looking woman, someone I've seen in your lab, maybe, but if she recognizes me (my messy hair, double hospital gown, lorazepam eyes), she doesn't let it register on her face.

Burns tells us to sit in the courtyard. The ward is overfull, but depressives are so quiet you'd never know. When she unlocks the double doors, wet air rolls in, condensing in the bleachy beigeness. I realize that I haven't been outside in more than two days. We sit at a plastic table in the middle of a balding ten-by-ten square. There are four trees. Smells like Pine-Sol.

"Kimberly," the woman says, offering me her hand. "I'm your doctor's intern. Any questions?" She is reading from an index card.

"I'm a scientist, too," I say, maybe too enthusiastically. I can't tell, because the blue pill I took after breakfast makes me feel like I'm packed in cotton and talking through a long pipe. "Entomology! Maybe I've seen you? I used to have a friend in Neuropsych." I almost say your name, but I stop talking because her professional demeanor cracks for a second.

Looking me up and down, a cautionary tale, she says, "We'd better get started." Back to the note card. "Please describe what you see."

I.

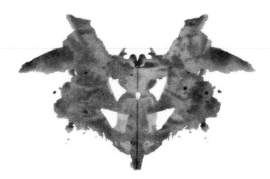

"A moth." It figures I'd say that. Every single person who sees this inkblot probably says "moth," or else "butterfly." Boring. But I stare at them all day, moths, their little dead bodies lined up on corkboard. So I also say, "A two-headed angel arguing with himself."

No response from Kimberly.

"The Halloween mask my little brother wore in 1989."

She scribbles something in her notepad.

"A rat face." That makes me think of you, but I don't say so.

Your rats flipped switches and navigated labyrinths. You taught them the rules. You were professional with them, but they seemed to like you. They came when you called. In your notebook I once read "Subjects respond best to unsalted peanuts," so I know you cared.

"Finished?" Kimberly asks.

"What?"

"Next card."

II.

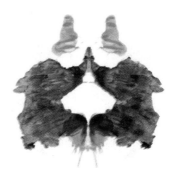

"A butterfly, there, and two creatures giving each other a high five."

"What kind of creatures?"

"Donkey-headed beasts, but more like bears. I don't know. I remember them from somewhere, like a cartoon or a dream."

"So you're saying they're bears?"

"I'm not explaining very well." I lean back in my wobbly plastic chair. The sunlight hurts my eyes.

"And the red shapes at the top are their faces?"

"I don't know what those are." I reach for the card. She places it faceup on the table and slides it toward me. The red blobs look like two obese centaurs, rearing. "Pentecostal flames?" I say. "Is it bad that I'm not seeing a cohesive image?"

"What do you mean by 'cohesive'?" Kimberly doesn't look up from her notebook.

"I'm seeing a bunch of disparate things."

Kimberly shakes her head. "So butterfly, bears, flames?"

"More like wolverines."

"Is that it?"

III.

"Two waiters, carrying a soup tureen. And there's the butterfly."

I guess it makes sense that they'd all have butterflies. Tempera-paint butterflies from kindergarten, the wet construction paper peeling. Squished paint inside—heavy, thick, and satisfying, coating the paper like peanut butter if you used just the right amount of water, but if you used too much, color dribbled onto the table.

I remember the story about your kindergarten class, how you told your teacher about the baby birds outside your window, and the whole class walked single file across the street to your front door, where your mom, surprised, reluctantly let you in. How everyone, holding hands with their field-trip buddies, took turns climbing onto the window seat to see the three screaming, naked blue jays. Only years later were you embarrassed to realize how strange it was to have your entire class in the crayon-scrawled pink bedroom, how unnaturally intimate.

"Is that all you see?" Kimberly wants this to end as quickly as possible.

"The elves floating behind the waiters' heads are giving them directions."

IV.

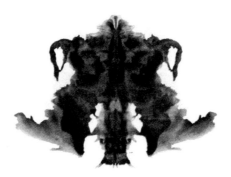

"The head of a wild boar. A baby dinosaur. A rat's skull." I wait while Kimberly codes her data.

Remember the day you showed me the rat skulls in your office, former research subjects lined up on the bookshelf, small to large? The largest as big as a tangerine; the smallest, barely a solid thing at all, a breath of bone, incomplete cranium like an exploded paper balloon. One in the middle: your favorite, Subject 47. "Exquisite cranial sutures," you said. And they were exquisite—cilium-small bone tendrils reaching out to one another, knitted together like the barbed feet of ivy runners.

I nod my head for Kimberly to continue.

V.

"That is clearly just a bat."

VI.

"A vagina totem pole?"

Kimberly is furiously coding. Probably she thinks I'm a serial killer. I search around for some other image to latch onto. Where are the butterflies now?

"Are you done?" Kimberly almost smiles. She looks up in my general direction at least. "I'm not supposed to say this, but if you're done . . . ?"

"Sure."

"It's amazing. Your response to the picture. Almost everyone says something like that!"

VII.

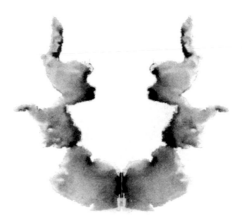

I stare at the card for a long time. Nothing. I lean on the table. There are water droplets on the surface. Too late for dew. How long until second meds? I look at the sky, and it is a low gray ceiling.

"Take your time," Kimberly says.

I try harder. "Faces?"

"Where?"

"Two different sets, maybe. Wait." I want to leave. My hands are sweaty, and more than anything I need to wash them. "Baby birds on a teeter-totter?"

"Okay." She holds the card, waiting.

"It's really more like an outline. The gray part doesn't seem important."

"The outline of what?"

"I don't know. Write down the other thing." I lean back in my chair. The plastic is so flimsy, I can make it bend.

VIII.

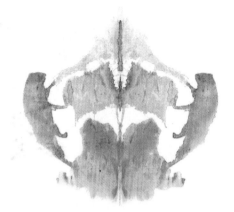

"Two baby rats, climbing onto a moth."

That night in The Rat Room, you told me that infant rat pups separated from their mothers emit a sound, a mewling, at a frequency undetectable by human ears. Other rats can hear it, though, and yours were restless in their cages. The inaudible ululation can continue for hours before the abandoned animal finally gives in to despair. In my hand, your last rat pup mouthed silent vowels.

"Next?"

IX.

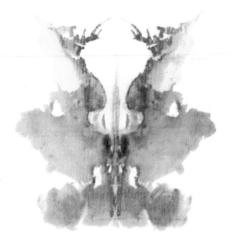

"A pelvis, which could also be a butterfly, which could also be a vagina."

"Only one to go," Kimberly says almost encouragingly, a good scientist: detached, like you.

In labs, orphaned rat pups are given every physical element needed for survival—nourishment, warmth, and simulated maternal heartbeats—but unless the mother rat is returned, the infants almost always die. Scientists can quantify. They can add and remove influencing physical factors. But it may be impossible to calculate the value of a missing piece.

"The whole thing?" Kimberly says.

"The spiky things are lobsters. They're fighting, but smiling."

X.

"A bunch of disparate stuff again," I say.

"Last one."

"The spiny things are crabs." I look at the blot and lean back in my chair. I don't say anything until Kimberly stops writing and starts tapping her pencil. "A weevil is ripping the sea slug in half, but it's holding together by a gut or a heartstring."

When you told me about the crying mice, I thought of the abstract influencing factors, the metaphysical properties. If the baby rats are any indication, the ephemeral connection between animals is inborn. The tether is essential for survival, but when severed, the component parts become malignant. In the case of the rats, oxygen intake lowers drastically. Immune functions cease. The once-sustaining bond withers to one-sided longing. The subject begins to doubt that a connection ever really existed. Longing corrodes into hopeless despair, and in this state the animal welcomes annihilation.

"Anything else?" Kimberly is already unzipping her backpack.

"Not really. Space dust? The green thing looks like a mustache."

Results

Back in the rec room, I resume my recording:

It is widely held that only two known elements lessen the detrimental physical effects manifested by the severance of the abstract property, herein referred to as [love]:

1. Time: arbitrary sequential structure applied to the occurrence of events and the intervals between
2. Space: boundaries imposed on a boundless dimension, based on the theoretical interplay between physical objects, given their proximity to other physical objects

For you, international research grants are a very good way to exit situations made uncomfortable by the interplay between physical objects. Half-hearted attempts at permanently exiting this boundless dimension led only to third-rate mental hospital purgation for me.

We hadn't spoken in three weeks. I thought you were visiting your sister. By my calculations it was our third, possibly fourth, breakup and not the longest.

I received your email—*Moved to Abu Dhabi*—and wrecked my car. In the four-hour interim between these two events, substances were consumed. The responding officer was nice enough to take me to the emergency room instead of jail, probably because I never made it out of the laboratory parking lot.

At the hospital there were questions and injections, samples of all kinds, and later I moved from one hospital to another in a barred-windowed van. The zeppelin-me floated in the valley between mountainous nurses. At some point they took my clothes. I woke up under industrially bleached blankets, wearing skidproof socks.

The doctor told me to focus on the negative, to make a list of the bad things between us, to acknowledge the necessity of endings. I could only think of four things:

1. I always knew that I was an experiment, another one of your rats crawling through the maze: electrocution/reward, electrocution/reward. I could see the pattern, and I thought because I understood, I was somehow outside the parameters, that I was special. Evidence does not support that conclusion.

2. Once, you kissed me in the stairwell and then, not five minutes later, in front of a crowd of your colleagues, pushed me away and said, "Who are you?"

3. The last time, you came to my house after midnight and climbed into my bed. Then, in the morning, I loaned you my blue oxford shirt, buttoned every button except the very top, and leaned in to kiss you. You turned away and said, "Sometimes I think I could love you, but you're so broken, probably too much trouble to fix."

4. In the two years I knew you, that was the third and final time you used the word "love" in my presence. I, on the other hand, choked it back constantly, "loves" upon "loves" floating up behind my molars, damming up the flow of language.

After I compiled my list, the doctor seemed pleased. So I tried to tell him about the good things—Thanksgivings with your family; the time in the coat closet at the Entomology Department Halloween party; how when you've just woken up, with blinky eyes and snaggled hair, you look like a baby dinosaur; the day in December when I forgot my mittens, so you loaned me one of yours and held my other hand inside your coat pocket while we walked across the slushy campus.

The doctor said none of that matters.

———

Maybe your rat ate her babies so that they would never leave her. Or maybe it was an attempt at time travel, back to before, when there was only her own need.

———

Days are measured in pills and Dixie cups. I pad out of the ward to the cafeteria three times a day with the other patients from Unit A: nonviolent, safe from skidding in our identical mint-green socks.

"A few more days," the admitting nurses say every time I ask.

I pace our unit hallway for hours every day. The nurses let me make the decaf, because my hands don't shake. I stole two golf pencils from the doctor's office to keep notes, but they disappeared from my sock drawer this morning during breakfast. If I write alone, in my room, it means that I am displaying antisocial behavior patterns. If I write at the table with the droolers and screamers, it's called art therapy.

Before I met you, love was certain but dead, a perfect luna moth specimen alighted heavily on a black-lit, sugar-washed bedsheet. You could creep up while its furred feet were stuck in the syrup and sweep it into the kill jar. Wings furiously scaling chartreuse, then slowing, slowing, stilled. You could keep her forever, fixed behind glass.

Data

$$\frac{(\text{neural pathways forged by animal interaction})^{86 \text{ nights in your bed}} + (\text{pheromone pull of woodsmoke} | \text{fresh bread})}{(\text{anxious}) \text{ avoidant attachment}} = [\text{love}]$$

Conclusions

Data is inconclusive and impossible to accurately compile. No doubt this is entirely due to human error. The duration and resilience of love is as yet unknown, but if there was a moment when said property became manifest it was this:

"What happens?" I asked. The room was warm from so much rodent respiration, ammonia, decomposing print and pulp, a lightbulb's worth of burnt energy radiating from each of our bodies. The blind fetal creature in my palm raised its rubber skull and howled mutely, more vibration left than life. You hung your lab coat on the back of the door. We could get formula, heat lamps. Behind me, you wrapped your arms around my waist; the wool of your sweater, almost soft, snagged the dry skin of my elbow.

Squinting into the cavern of my cupped palms, you rested your chin on my shoulder, your mouth so close to my ear that I felt the condensation of your breath, liquid-hot on my neck.

"You peer over your glasses like a librarian," you said. "I love that." Hand outstretched in a simulacrum of gentleness, you offered the doomed rat the tip of your finger, and for a moment she mistook it for comfort.

About the Author

KILBY ALLEN, a native of the Mississippi Delta, received her MFA from Brooklyn College, where she was awarded both the Himan Brown Award and the Lainoff Prize in 2010. While living in New York, she worked in the literary department at Symphony Space and helped with the production of WNYC's *Selected Shorts*. Currently, she is a PhD candidate and Kingsbury Fellow at Florida State University. Her work has appeared or is forthcoming in such journals as *Nashville Review*, *Drunken Boat*, and the *Baltimore Review*.

Brooke Weeber © 2014

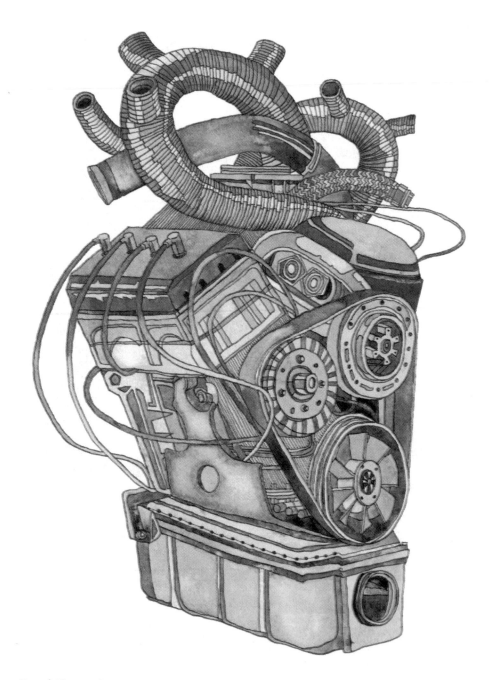

Forsyth Harmon © 2013

SHEILA

REBECCA ADAMS WRIGHT

Today, sipping tea from a faded mug and sitting in front of his computer in running pants and sneakers, John grieved over yet another article about the demise of robotic pets. Sheila lay quietly beside his desk, shifting only when the rollers of his chair came too close to the fur of her belly or the brush of her undocked tail. Every so often while he read, John would put a hand on the dog's head. He did this the way another man might rub his wedding ring or lay a hand on his crotch—to reassure himself that despite a harsh reality, the important things were still there.

Articles like the one he was reading had become common, and the gist was always the same. Computerized pets were clumsy, soulless, dangerously high voltage, hard to catch and eliminate should their programming malfunction, etc. Why had people ever bought them? What was the problem with good old-fashioned flesh and blood anyway? The author of this particular piece, a Cassidy Sim from Albany, New York, called for "the rounding up and incinerating of the last of the dinosaurs," a "massive purge of those evolutionary dead ends not already laid to rest by the meteor shock of Ginger Creek."

John sighed. Why did he do this to himself? He reached over to turn off the monitor and pushed himself up from the chair with a wince.

Ginger Creek. His troublesome hip was bothering him again. Ginger Creek be damned. Those dogs were feral, never serviced; they were nothing like Sheila.

Eager for the next phase of their morning ritual, Sheila rose from her position under the desk. Her moist eyes followed John's progress toward the kitchen. When he reached the doorway and turned to call her, she waggled her hind end and leaped lightly to the kitchen, patting the tiled surface of the counter with her white paws. This was the same reaction she had given him for years. She was slower now, her ball joints stiffer, but the sight of her small paws dancing along the blue tile never failed to make him smile.

"My goodness," John said. He peered into the cabinets before him and raised a hand to his face in mock despair. "Dear me. I seem to have forgotten to buy dog biscuits. It seems there's no treat today."

"Aoo!"

"Biscuits?"

"Aoo!"

"There are biscuits here, you say?"

"Ar-oo!"

"Where, girl? Where are the biscuits?" He lowered himself into one of Millie's old Mission-style kitchen chairs and waited for the aging dog to sniff her way along the bottom row of cabinets. Today he had hidden her rubber biscuit in the tiny cupboard under the sink. It was easiest for him to access it there, with the cabinet's built-in lazy Susan.

"Rark!" Sheila stood at slender, pretty point. John had never been much of a hunter, but he loved this stance. All alertness and focus. Not unlike his own bones, Sheila's parts were wearing down, but there were advantages to being mostly metal and microchips. Fur, sockets, individual wires—all these parts could be replaced. As long as her programming held, as long as she could lick oil into the joints of her feet and legs, his dog would be able to compose herself nearly as beautifully as she had in her first year. There was a joy in looking at her and watching the years drop away. He would never understand how anyone could call an animal as graceful as Sheila "clumsy."

While he was drinking coffee and Sheila was gnawing at the same treat she gnawed at every morning, the phone rang.

Please don't be Richard.

"How you doing, Dad?" John could hear his son David's students in the background. Rat-a-tat-rat-a-tat-rat-a-tat-a-tat-tat.

"Drum solos?" he asked.

"Practice for Saturday's game," David said. The snares were muffled just enough to sound like an approaching army. "We're working on sticking with the beat." A hand over the phone. "Keep together, guys! Keep it going just like that." The hand removed. "Sorry. I wanted to know if you'd talked to Richard yet."

"Why?"

"Dad . . ." David sighed. "You haven't, have you? Have you called him?"

"The business between Richard and me," John said, feeling as prickly as he knew he sounded, "is nobody else's business. And frankly, it's none of Richard's damn business either."

"It sucks, Dad. I know. Trust me—I know better than anyone how bad it sucks. But you could lose your pension going against the county like this."

"To hell with my pension."

David sighed again. The drums behind him, metallic and sharp, snapped off beats like rubber bands. Rat-tat-rat-a-tat-tat-tat.

"Just promise me that if he doesn't call by tonight, you'll call him."

"You better get back to those kids. They're losing cohesion."

"Tell me about it. It's called high school. But Dad—"

"It was good of you to call, Son."

"Talk to Richard," David said again before hanging up. "Please. I love her too, but she's only a dog. Mom wouldn't have wanted to see you screw up your good name over this."

———

David, well-intentioned as he was, couldn't remember Millie the way John did. Quiet, stubborn, brilliant Millie. John returned to the table and sipped his coffee slowly, thinking of her. His wife had been proud of him, yes, and proud of his work. Millie's support was a source of comfort when he found himself agonizing over a particularly difficult draft of an opinion; it helped him, knowing that she invested a great deal of herself in being the wife of a circuit court judge. But Millie had also loved Sheila.

Some of their neighbors had balked at being introduced to a "mechanimal," as pets like Sheila had occasionally been called then. But Millie had been as gentle and happy with the computerized dog as with the biological terriers she had owned in her rural youth. Up until the day she died, his wife could call Sheila to her with nothing more than a jangle of her turquoise bracelets. No matter where she was—asleep on their platform bed, watching for the mail truck, poking through the tall grass with David—the spaniel would come running.

John had been convinced there was something about Millie's illness that Sheila could sense. It was impossible for him not to think so, watching the liver-and-white head settle onto his wife's narrow lap, the amber eyes follow every small gesture that passed between partners. Even now, each of Millie's many gestures, sounds, and scents was probably stored somewhere in Sheila's incorruptible memory.

Perhaps that was one of the many reasons he loved her, her ability to hold on to these details. When Millie died, only Sheila seemed as inconsolable as John. Sheila was his companion when David started school, joined the hockey team, the swim team, became a teenager, went to college. And now it was Sheila who kept him from dreading the long, lonely expanse of the retirement he had always expected to share with his wife.

Millie had been the one to nickname Sheila "our little lady." He had caught Millie, once, with the dog's beautiful wedge-shaped head in her hands, outlining very seriously Sheila's responsibilities to John and David once she was gone. She would never have wanted him to abandon the companion who still tied them together. A companion now, who—Lord, how time could fly—had stuck beside him for an astounding twenty-five years.

But still, there was Ginger Creek. John didn't understand it any more than anyone else. There were hundreds of possible explanations for why those three dogs had turned on the children they were programmed to protect—poor socialization, lack of adequate servicing, a tiny flaw in the motherboard of their brains. And there were just as many preventative measures to keep those failures from occurring again. But the consequences of the tragedy were clear. Less than a month after Randy, Jason, and Asia Dupree were torn to pieces in their own backyard, forty of the forty-seven states that had originally signed off on computerized pets were repealing the legislation. By Monday, owning Sheila would be a crime. And that couldn't be avoided.

———

Every website John had searched had extolled the virtues of the Brittany spaniel. Intelligent, obedient, and cheerful dogs, they were good with children, friendly with strangers, and eager to please their masters. The booklet that came with Sheila had included a "care and maintenance" DVD that also emphasized, among other things, that Brittanys need to be given access to water.

"Whether hunting accessory or apartment companion," the smiling young woman had told him, stroking the head of a mechanical spaniel taller and more prissily groomed than Sheila, "your Brittany has been meticulously engineered to American Kennel Club breed specifications. All of our working models are designed to withstand high pressures and extended exposure to water. Remember: your pet has been carefully programmed to exhibit desires appropriate to its breed. Be sure to run your new friend and get out to the lake or pool just as often as you can. Your Brittany will thank you for it."

This need to "wet the dog" (as Millie called it) was not something John had anticipated. The first time he and David placed her in water—in a half-full kiddie pool purchased for the purpose—he was sure that the dog's circuits would fry before their eyes, spitting and popping before her lifeless body slid beneath the surface. But Sheila seemed to enjoy the experience. She stood for a moment, wagging her brushy tail, and then sat down, soaked up to her belly with no ill effects. "Mom, come see!" David had run to bring Millie to the door. She stood there supporting herself on the door frame, too thin, a scarf around what remained of her dark hair, and watched the happy dog pant in the afternoon sun.

"Our girl knows something more than you do, John." She laughed, and the ring of it had been nice to hear. During those last stages of her illness, Millie had rarely laughed. Sheila, delighted to have pleased her people, had hopped from the pool and rolled her dripping body ecstatically on the grass. She chased a squealing David around the yard, soaking him so thoroughly when she pinned him down to lick him that John had to carry both boy and dog inside wrapped in towels.

After that John took the advice of his current law clerk, a mad-for-gadgets legal student named Louise who loved the idea of his computerized pet and had done some breed research of her own.

"You should take her to Ipson's Lake," Louise had said. "Throw something into the water and tell her to bring it back. She'll go ape, Judge. Spaniels are practically as in love with the water as retrievers." It seemed to be true. John and David, carrying thermoses, sandwiches, and binoculars in canvas backpacks, could never keep up with Sheila as she ran down the bumpy dirt trail to the lake. Every Saturday morning Sheila waited by the door, whining. In the car, she pressed her nose to the window, waiting to spring out. And as soon as the door opened, she was off, shooting toward the trail, returning to dance around John, then running ahead again. When they were close enough to smell the water, she took off in earnest and they always heard the splash well before they could see her narrow, elegant head bobbing on the surface of the water.

Ipson's Lake wasn't a true lake at all, but a flooded quarry that had once belonged to the Ipson Brick Factory, now collapsing quietly in the rural weeds a half mile to the north. The water was surprisingly clean. In the summer, when John and David brought their swimsuits, they sometimes found the quarry populated by other families or by sunbathing teenagers, who rose on their elbows to glance at them over mirrored sunglasses before slipping back down to the towels they had laid across the sandy bank.

But because they came early, they were usually alone. John liked it best that way. He enjoyed the opportunity to be in a place where no one knew him, where relative strangers wouldn't ask for an opinion on awkward personal matters or tell yet another lame judicial joke for his benefit. It was a relief to have a few hours to let go of all the office pressures—trials, pretrials, motion hearings, draft after draft of judicial opinion—and of his concerns about Millie. Sometimes, during the week, his chest would constrict at the thought of her absence. He couldn't picture a house where the paperback books didn't all have spines broken by Millie's one-handed reading, where the pillows she was constantly fluffing didn't smell of her orange-scented skin cream. His fear of her oncoming death grew so all-encompassing that he found it hard to breathe, and had to clutch the arm of his chair or the collar of his own robe until the feeling passed.

At those moments he was convinced he could not go on without her, but it was the weekend hours at Ipson's Lake that gave him the strength to think maybe he could. He and his son would peel the Saran Wrap from their sandwiches and roll it into balls, dirty side in, the way David's kindergarten teacher had taught him. They stuffed the balls into the front pockets of their backpacks and drank the noodle soup in their canteens. Then, while David hunted for rocks and snail shells fascinating enough to take home to his mother, John would find a comfortable place to sit, feet pressed into the warm sand, and watch Sheila swim.

Paddling there, the dog filled up the anxious, empty parts of him. All the circles and rectangles of her body drew away from each other and then came back together in long, muscular movements. Her vitality was electrifying. It was complete. John couldn't help but draw comparisons. On the shore there was David, blood and bone, scrambling about happy and alive. In the water there was Sheila, riveted seams and contained electric current, but just as active, just as happy. And at home there was his wife, dying by degrees. There was no escaping the irony of it all—computerized Sheila's undeniable life and organic Millie's inescapable decline.

———

After his conversation with David, John was too restless for any of the activities he normally indulged in before lunch. Crossword puzzles, morning talk shows, bird-watching, and web-surfing . . . they were all too tame, too cheerful. He had become such a harmless old man. When, he wondered, had he stopped participating in the world and begun merely observing it? In the courtroom, of course, he had always needed to hold himself impartial, apart, but his rulings meant something. They were like the stones David had always loved to throw into Ipson's Lake: they rippled out into the world and changed it, if only slightly. Now he was subject to someone else's ruling, and the dread was like a lead sinker attached to his heart.

"Come on, old girl. Let's go throw tennies." Sheila scrambled to her feet, and he grabbed the mesh bag of tennis balls hanging from the door of the hall closet. Anyone who entered his house would think he owned a pack of dogs—rubber bones in the cabinets, squeaky toys in Millie's old knitting basket, dog blankets bunched up at the foot of the couch, tennis balls on the door. John didn't believe in hiding his things from visitors. The house was clean and mostly orderly, so why pretend he didn't like a little clutter?

The front yard was surprisingly bright after his morning indoors. A group of sparrows, startled from the hanging birdbath, took off in a flapping brown cloud and set the bowl swinging like a censer.

"Go get it, Sheila!" John threw a tennis ball off toward the pines that shielded his white clapboard house from Neil's. His neighbor used to bring his twin eight-year-old girls over to play with Sheila, but hadn't since Ginger Creek.

"It's not Sheila," Neil explained one afternoon when the two men ran into each other at the hardware store. "Jill and Katie are crazy about her. But I'm their father. I have to look out for their best interests. If I let them play with Sheila, how can I keep them away from other computerized animals, maybe ones that haven't been kept up the way yours has?"

Sheila came back with the ball tucked proudly between her enameled teeth. "Good girl." John threw again, this time into the tall grass between the house and the unpaved road. "Take me to it," he said, and followed her out to where the mowed lawn ended. Neil's words ran through his head while he watched her furry body step here and there, picking through the fallen brush in search of the tennis ball. He realized, sadly, that he was out of options. To men like Neil, Sheila wasn't real. She was a memento, perhaps a dangerous memento, and she was something to be destroyed. An object as unfeeling as a car. Easy to destroy.

———

John had known from the very first minute, running his hand down the dog's spine, feeling the fine fur roll silkily under his hand, that she was perfect. Her beautiful lines; her strong, straight head; the way her face was cut like bread, into wedges of brown on a background of white and dotted with crumbs of freckles—all of these things informed her rightness, her perfectness. He had had the sudden thought that she stood exactly as tall as the radiator whose humming had lulled him to sleep in his childhood home. When he stroked her, her tail swung back and forth in arcs that mirrored a half grin. She was a dog with dignity and personality, too noble for the discount computer warehouse.

"Never going to find another model as nice as this at sale price." Just moments after John and David had walked into the store, a bearded salesman had hustled them out of the depressing main showroom—an industrial-beige box full of cellular devices, computer parts, and office electronics—and into a small alcove. The room was decorated like a den. John knew that the atmosphere here was supposed to sell him on the homeyness, the Americana of the whole idea. It was supposed to be sumptuous, but by the look of things, it had inherited the furnishings of a cheap model home. Surfaces were laminated particleboard; books were leather shells bereft of pages. The fireplace that David dropped to his knees to crawl into was only a front and left the boy bewildered. "I've seen units not nearly as nice as this one go for five figures at Circuit World," the salesman said.

John had wanted the salesman to leave them, allow him and his son time to discover the dog in their own way, but the man was determined to pursue the aggressive sale. He began to recite durability figures and processing speeds. When John laid his fingers against the dog's cool nose, the salesman watched him touch the leathery nostrils and said "cooling fan."

"She's pretty." John glanced down. David, hardly tall enough to reach the dog where she stood on display, had abandoned the false fireplace in order to press himself up against the laminated wood of her pedestal. He stood, petting one of her slim back paws with a tender intensity he rarely exhibited. "What kind of dog is she, Dad?"

"This here is an A-plus approximation of a Brittany spaniel," the salesman said. He was answering David but looking at John, a habit John had found distasteful in his son's youth and intolerable once he began to grow old and people's rudeness had reversed. Now clerks and cashiers were just as likely to respond to David as to John when the two of them were together and the elder man was speaking.

"Is she real?" his son asked. John remembered how David had looked up at him, waiting for some kind of reassurance. He remembered, too, how the salesman had jumped in before he could reply.

"Real as your phone and your television!" The salesman slapped the dog's haunch with a veracity that made John want to strangle him. Yes, he had felt a kinship with the patient animal almost immediately. He liked the way she didn't shrink from them after the blow, but didn't react with irritation either. She was like a well-rooted tree in a storm. Whatever went on around her and whatever acted upon her, John was sure she would function with consistent affection. He had to admit that the husband and father in him were attracted to that.

The salesman had started to tell him how safe the dog was, how closely programmed to breed specifics, but John ignored him the way he was learning to ignore foolish and overly garrulous attorneys who came before him in his new position on the circuit court bench.

"Yes," he had said to David, answering the important question, "computers make her work, but she's real. Do you think Mom will like her?"

"Maybe she can make Mom better."

"Maybe so." Looking into the dog's mournful amber eyes, John had felt sure that this was true. "Maybe if Mom feels better that will help her to get well."

"I like her. She doesn't make me sneeze. Let's take her home, Dad."

And, as if she understood what had been said, the dog crouched down and licked the top of David's head once, twice. Later, John slid the receipt of his payment for her into a drawer with a wedding photo and one of David's baby pictures. That receipt was still there, pressed between loved faces, proof of the best purchase he ever made.

———

John sat at the table with the telephone in his hand. He stared at it. Looked away. Looked at it again. Sheila was on the floor beside him, snoozing. He looked away. He hadn't felt such helpless anger since Millie died. Then, she had been the betrayer. Now he would be. And either way, it amounted to his being left behind.

Richard didn't pick up until the fourth ring.

"Jackson County Sheriff's Department. Sheriff Richard Nett."

"It's John."

There was a long sigh. "Shit, John. I didn't think you were going to call. Thought you were going to make me hunt you down."

Like some kind of criminal.

"And I thought it might make sense to talk some more about this."

"John—"

"I've never put myself above the law, Richard. You know that. I've got no more and no fewer rights than any other citizen in this county. But I also happen to know I'm one of the only people affected by this ruling, and it's wrong. It's wrong, Richard."

"What am I supposed to do?" His old friend's voice was tired. "I've known that ridiculous mutt of yours longer than I've known my own kids. I'm sick about this. But the law is the law. You want me to start making exceptions every time I don't agree with what comes down the pipes?"

"It's such a small exception," John said quietly.

"You don't mean that."

"You'd be surprised."

"Look. I'll do everything I can to make it as gentle as possible. I'm not a monster. You can sit right there with her, even hold her if you want. The officers will leave the room as soon as you tell them to. Sheila won't feel a thing. She won't even know what's happening."

"What if I don't bring her? What if I don't goddamn bring her?"

"Then I'll come and get her," Richard said. "And you'll be off your position as visiting judge and off your state pension. Please. Don't break my fucking heart."

———

John was forever amazed by the things people did for love—love of other people, of drugs, of money, of the rush. How many divorces, how many criminal trials, how many long and impassioned disputes had he sat through in the course of his career? How many times had elated plaintiffs pumped his hand? Grateful defendants? How often had he been shielded by his officers from those who were hurt and believed he was the one who had wronged them? John could scarcely remember. In fact, as he climbed the stairs, favoring his bad hip, he could recall only fleeting impressions of his entire working life, which, like every other aspect of his youth, now seemed to have passed so quickly.

It wasn't Richard's fault that he had forced the tough decision. The law was larger than two men, and contained its own currents they had become caught up in. David would be angry and unhappy, but he was an adult, and would understand. John was proud of the man his son had become.

Upstairs, John sat for a long time on the bed he had shared with Millie, stroking Sheila's warm head. The mattress had been replaced years ago, but the old wooden frame was the same. Same old scratches, same old squeaks. His wife had died, but he had never been able to write her out of their home. Her clothes and shoes were gone, but nothing else. He had given away only the simple, the practical. He couldn't part with the rest. He supposed that was his greatest struggle, parting with things.

"But not you," he told the spaniel. "Don't you worry."

He flipped on the light in the master bathroom and pulled the cleaning supplies out from under the sink. He tugged on the yellow rubber gloves and began to scrub the freestanding bathtub with abrasive orange cleaner. The slight ring around the bottom disappeared quickly, and he snapped the gloves into the trash can, packed the various chemicals back into their cupboard. In the bright bathroom light, the porcelain was so white, it was almost blue. Rinsing the tub with a gallon jug of hot water, John felt like an old prospector who had carved a bed out of Yukon ice. He put in the stopper and let the warm water run.

While the tub was filling, he sloughed off his athletic clothes and stood in front of the armoire, debating. His clothes were so familiar. There they hung, pressed, stable, comforting as old friends. He fingered the cuff of a shirt he had worn to court countless times. The fabric was just a shade darker than ivory, a color that had flattered him before his dark hair went gray. Though he had chosen it himself, it looked just like something Millie might have purchased for him.

He slid the shirt off its hanger and buttoned it around his throat. He added a navy suit coat and matching blue slacks. Around his neck went one of the silk ties David had given him last Christmas, his hands dreaming themselves through the Windsor knot. Out of the bureau came the silver cuff links Millie had given him for their fifth anniversary. That was the year David was born, and John remembered giving her a locket with his baby picture glued inside. He shined and slid on his oxfords.

The tub was full. John turned the tap and watched the water settle, doing his best to clear his mind. He tried to steel himself for what had to be done. Three deep breaths. One. Two. Now. If he didn't do it now, they would take her from him.

"Here, Sheila," he called, making his voice as cheerful as he could. When the dog was in front of him, he took the wedge of her face between his palms and stared into those marvelous amber eyes. "Don't worry," he told her again. As soon as he spoke, her tail began to swing slowly back and forth. "I promise this won't hurt, old girl."

And then his knobby fingers broke apart two of the plastic brackets holding closed the lynchpin of her sternum and pried open a few inches of the dog's feathered breast. Inside was a nest of wires and circuits John had seen only when Sheila had been subject to her annual preventative service. Somewhere behind the humming voltage of the electronics and cooling apparatus was his sweet dog's mechanical heart. Even now, dust was beginning to settle inside its delicate mechanisms.

Sheila whined. "Steady," John said. He straightened up, adjusted his tie, and took one last look in the mirror. Staring back at him was an old man, older than any John knew. He bent down and took all thirty-three pounds of Sheila in his arms. The dog was comfortingly solid. Lifting from his knees, John hefted her as high as he could. Carefully, he placed one foot into the tub. He could feel the heat of her processor against his chest, a warm, whirring pulse close to his heart. He thought he might be crying. Sheila let out another uncertain whine, tried to turn and meet his eye as he put his other foot in the water.

"One more swim," John said. The room around him had grown so bright. "One more time, Sheila."

And he sat.

About the Author

REBECCA ADAMS WRIGHT is a former Zell Fellow and a graduate of the Clarion Science Fiction & Fantasy Writers' Workshop. She earned her MFA in fiction from the University of Michigan and has won both the Leonard and Eileen Newman Writing Prize and a late-night Emily Dickinson poetry challenge. Her fiction has appeared in *Daily Science Fiction* and her nonfiction in *Children's Literature in Education*. Her story collection *The Thing About Great White Sharks* will be published by Little A in February 2015. Rebecca lives in Ypsilanti, Michigan, with her husband and daughter.

Maryanna Hoggatt © 2014

THE INVASION COMMANDER'S MOTION FOR NEW BUSINESS

SHAENON K. GARRITY

CONTACT DATE+3.45.333u

Hello, is everyone here? There's myself, two, three . . . five. Good, that's great, that's as expected. First thing, I want to congratulate the team on an almost flawless landing and critical-point infection. As I can see from your convincingly mammalian faces, we've each managed to locate an endemic host, spore, then devour the host, absorb his knowledge of this planet, and take his shape. By-the-book infection—I'm sure the homeworld will be pleased.

. . . Or *her* shape. Yes, cC-3. Point taken, it doesn't hurt to recall they have two sexes here.

No, cC-6, that's usually one sex per individual. I think you're a little confused. cC-3, you're the expert. Would you say cC-6 has duplicated a "he" or a "she"?

A "he," really?

You agree, cC-5? That's interesting, that's really interesting.

No, cC-6, I'm willing to trust the group consensus on this one.

Honestly, you don't have to—

Yes, cC-6, that's definitely male. Put that away, please. Thank you.

We're getting ahead of ourselves. When I called tonight's meeting at this diner, I mentioned that the invasion so far has been almost flawless. I have been given to understand that aA Company landed on an uninhabitable planet and failed to spore, while contact with bB Company was lost within the local interstellar cloud. But we of cC Company made it, in spite of what the other companies and the Overmind may have had to say about us in the past, and that means it's time to get to work! Right?

Sadly, we have had a loss. It seems cC-2, my second-in-command, was discovered by the natives while still sporing, mistaken for a kohlrabi, and eaten. If we could have a moment of silence . . .

Kohlrabi. It's a vegetable. A root vegetable. A . . . a kind of turnip, I think.

I have cC-2's last transmission here, in fact. I think it would be a good idea to have a listen, difficult as it may be, to get an idea of the unique dangers . . . well, let's not say "dangers" . . . the unique challenges we face on this planet.

Cabbage? cC-5 is saying "cabbage." I don't know about that, cC-5, we don't look anything like cabbages in our gestating pod form. We—

A kohlrabi doesn't look like a cabbage. It looks like an immature pod. Come to think of it, what exactly is a kohl—?

I'll look it up. All right? We'll both look it up and get back to this at the next meeting.

I see cC-6 has a question. Yes?

Sautéed and tossed with mushrooms, according to intelligence . . .

No, I don't know how he tasted. What kind of question is that?

What, cC-5? You can also eat them raw? cC-5, we've been on this planet for three days. How do you know all this about kohlrabi?

Never mind. Just . . . never mind. Before we break and return to our respective beachheads to locate additional hosts and reproduce, I want to thank cC-4, our pilot, for doing such a great job with the landing. Wasn't that a great landing? And didn't he find us a perfect high-density metropolitan area in which to begin our conquest of the planet? San Francisco—what a city, huh?

Yes, you're right, cC-3. Didn't *she* find us a great area. The point is, I think we should all give cC-4 a hand.

It's a colloquial phrase. From my host's brain. It means to put your hands together and clap.

They're those things at the ends of your arms.

These. These are arms. These are hands. How did you get all that about kohlrabi and not know—?

No, cC-6. That's not an arm. I tell you what, let's break and save this for the next meeting, what do you say?

CONTACT DATE+35.89.004u

Good to see you all again. I'm eager to hear how many humans each of you has killed and replaced since last month's meeting. cC-3, why don't we start with you?

Wait, I see cC-5 raising his hand. That's *hand*, everyone, I trust we've all learned which parts are our hands now. I appreciate your enthusiasm, cC-5, but unless this is an emergency, let's stick to numerical order. If you would, cC-3 . . . ?

It *is* an emergency? Oh . . . well, then, let me see what you've got on that sheet of paper.

"Kohlrabi (German turnip) is a low, stout cultivar of the cabbage. Its origin in nature is the same as that of cabbage, broccoli, cauliflower, kale, collard greens, and Brussels sprouts." Well. That's. Well.

Five minutes on Wikipedia, you say? Well. Er. You know, this is very educational, cC-5, and I applaud your initiative, but what do you say we get back to the conquest? You remember the conquest? cC-3, your turn.

No, cC-3, I did not interrupt you because you're a woman. I'm in a female body myself, in case you haven't noticed. You saw what happened. cC-5 just barged in with this—

No, of course your contribution to the invasion is more important than whether kohlrabi is a cabbage or a turnip.

Well, I'm sorry, cC-5, but it is! Please, cC-3, tell the group exactly how many soldier drones you've added to our forces.

Zero. But you met a guy at a grocery co-op and you think you might infect him? Okay. That's not as good as I was hoping, but it's progress. cC-4, how many drones have you created and stationed at your beachhead?

You got evicted from your beachhead on a noise complaint. She waved a Swiffer at you until you went away. No, I'm sure it wasn't your fault.

Your landlady is a what? Well, all the more reason to kill her and spore into her carcass. All right. cC-5?

I thought it only took five minutes, cC-5. If it was only five minutes, you can't have spent the entire past lunar cycle on "research."

If that's how you're going to be, you can have your paper back. cC-6, I hope you've had more luck with the sporing and . . . er . . . so forth . . .

I'm sorry, but has anyone here successfully snatched any bodies at *all*?

Well, no, but I've been very busy in communion with the Overmind. It's not all fun and games being invasion commander, you know.

Look, I just want to get this puny planet conquered. You want bB Company to show us up to the homeworld? You know what they're like. I'm sure wherever they landed, they've got their planet half-infected by now, and all we have are these five bodies we're wearing. I don't want to be too hard on you all, but this is an order. The moment you walk out this door, you have to get serious about conquest. Understood?

Good. Great. Now let's—

No, I will not.

That's not important. This isn't about me. This is about taking over the Earth.

Fine, then, I *will* put it up to a vote. How many people here want me to—?

All of you? Really? Even you, cC-3?

All right, all right. I was wrong for thinking the kohlrabi was part of the turnip family. Happy?

CONTACT DATE+62.93.17u

Where is cC-4? I'm serious. It's bad enough that we had to wait an hour for cC-6 to finish his shift at the coffee shop, but we actually need cC-4.

I'm sorry, cC-6. You're right, that was unfair.

Yes, and a little hurtful. I've just been on edge lately.

cC-4 is where? In Portland? What is she doing in Portland?

Crashing with whom?

So what I'm hearing is, cC-4 moved to Portland because she couldn't find an apartment in San Francisco.

Sorry, couldn't find an apartment outside the Tenderloin, and yes, I agree it's a little scary there. You know what's supposed to be scarier than the Tenderloin, everyone? An army of killer brain-sucking pod people from outer space!

No, I'm not talking about bB Company. I'm talking about us! I'll have you know that while you've been lounging around, I've assimilated two humans. That's right, two.

They're out scouting additional hosts, that's where.

Er. Bill. Bill and . . . Trixie. Bill and Trixie Pepper. You'll address them as cC-1a and cC-1b, of course. When you meet them. Does anyone have cC-4's number in Portland?

Oh, for cripes' sake. I'm tabling everything until next month. Are you happy?

CONTACT DATE+97.50.00u

First, let me apologize for getting a little testy at the last meeting. Several of you texted me afterward to comment that I seemed on edge. That was unprofessional of me. Also, I've taken into consideration the suggestion—made by most of you, in fact—that you could get more killing and assimilation done if I'd make some accommodations of my own. As you can see, I've rescheduled our briefings to meet at lunchtime to accommodate everyone's busy schedules.

Yes, cC-6, I'm sorry, I know you work the night shift at the coffee shop now and it's hard for you to get up by noon. We all appreciate your dedication. Can we give cC-6 a hand?

Yes! Just like that! We've really come far, haven't we?

Before we go any further, let me tell you how proud I am that one of us has finally produced a soldier drone. cC-3, when you walked in here with this young man, it was such a weight off my . . .

He's not a drone? He's just an unassimilated human? Then why on earth did you bring him to our secret planetary-conquest meeting?

That's the stupidest answer I've ever heard.

Well, it is. It's like none of you are taking this invasion seriously. This is exactly what the Overmind said would happen. Honestly, it makes me want to scream sometimes, one of those high-pitched screams where your jaw hangs open and your eyes roll back into your—

cC-3, wait! Let's talk this over like adults! cC-3, so help me, if you walk out that door—

Well, that could have gone better. So . . . for this meeting we're down to cC-5, cC-6, and myself. Does anyone else have a report to make? I mean real news, not—

Why, thank you, cC-6. A postcard for *Flexible Lola's Vegetarian Burlesque Show* in Oregon. What does this have to do with anything?

cC-4 is Lola. Of course.

As long as we're airing our laundry, I have a confession to make. The item I submitted at the last meeting about assimilating two humans . . . that was not entirely accurate. The truth is, it was somewhat fewer than two. In fact, it was no humans. None. I thought I could get a couple before today's meeting and make up the difference.

No, I don't want a hug. I'm a terrible invasion commander. I haven't had the nerve to commune with the Overmind in weeks. I have to go home and rewrite our entire strategy. cC-5, could you find cC-3 and her . . . you know, the human? I didn't get his name, sorry.

What kind of name is Richmond?

Meeting adjourned. I don't even know anymore . . . Say, can anyone pick up the check?

CONTACT DATE+120.50.00u

So! Here we are, together again! Except for Lola, of course, who is touring the state of Washington with her burlesque troupe. Let's all wish her the best and hope she manages to devour a few humans along the way. And let's welcome the newest member of the invasion force, Richmond. He's a mere Earthman but has assured me that as long as cC-3 wants to conquer the world for the Overmind, he wants to conquer the world for the Overmind, too.

Have a Kleenex, cC-6.

Men—and women, and women—I've given the matter a lot of thought, and I've decided we need to change our approach. We've been spending all our time at our individual spore nests, seeing each other only for these meetings, when we should be working together. I mean, we're pod people. That's our great strength, cooperation. Am I right?

Exactly. So I propose we all sign up for the grocery co-op and focus our efforts on selecting and devouring victims there. First the co-op, then the world!

I'm feeling good about this. I don't mind telling you, I feel very good. Also, Richmond tells me we can get discounts on bulk granola.

CONTACT DATE+133.82.433u

I think you all know why I've called you here. After discussing the issue individually with each of you and weighing all our options, I've reached a decision. Our next victim will be Rob, the assistant manager at the co-op.

Yes, all right, our *first* victim, if you want to be all glass-half-empty, Richmond. Let me remind you that your brain would've been devoured by spores months ago if it weren't for cC-3.

I'm not threatening him, cC-3, I'm just pointing out the obvious.

We're getting off track. Rob. The assistant manager. Through my analysis of the data, I've determined that he has the genetic qualities of an easily convertible host, as well as personal habits that will make it easy for us to isolate and subdue him. Also, we all really hate that guy for taking away our olive-bar privileges.

The plan is to stay after hours, corner him at the office, chloroform him, and launch into basic sporing-and-assimilation procedure as we learned back on the good old homeworld. I trust we all remember the procedure, yes?

cC-6, you've acquired the chloroform? Maybe? I hope?

Good! You followed through on a task! I'm surprised. I mean impressed. I'm surprised by how impressed I am, cC-6. Excellent work. So once he's unconscious, I'll spore into his—

You want us to infect Rob with *your* spores? I don't like to pull rank, cC-5, but I am invasion commander, and if there are options, I'd kind of like to be the first to produce a drone. How would it look if we created a cC-5a drone before a cC-1a drone?

I'll tell you—it'd look ridiculous. bB Company would laugh at me. Us. They'd laugh at us. So, cC-6, if you could give me the chloroform?

cC-6? Hello?

What do you mean, you're more than just a number? I know you're more than just a—

I refuse to call you Heather.

No, it's perfectly fair that Richmond has a name and you don't. He's a human. Humans have names. What are you going to call your soldier drones, Heather-b through Heather-zzz-prime?

I'll pretend I didn't hear that.

Fine. Everyone, from now on we'll call him Heather. cC-5, *both* of us will spore into Rob the assistant manager. Anything to get this invasion under way.

Now let's go get that jerk.

CONTACT DATE+135.02.219u

As invasion commander, I feel it's important to go over the events of last night and think about exactly where we went wrong. It's not going to be pleasant, but as I see it, there are several points we can turn into learning experiences. Learning experiences, everyone, all right? No one's pointing fingers.

First, as we were getting ready to drive to the co-op, Lola arrived at my doorstep with four burlesque dancers—none of whom, I should note, seemed to be soldier drones—in what I'm told were tear-away *Jonny Quest* fetish costumes. Lola herself was dressed as . . . what was it?

"Naughty Hadji." Right.

For reasons I'm not so clear on, Lola insisted on joining us for the assimilation, taking her troupe along because . . . why *was* that, Lola?

Because you'd only rented the one bus. Right. I suppose I'm glad you've been reading the minutes I forwarded to you in Portland. That's . . . something.

Yes, everyone, it's great to see Lola again. I probably wasn't clear enough about that at the time. I was a little preoccupied. At the co-op, we did manage to corner Rob in his office. Let's take a moment to congratulate ourselves on that. Good work, everybody. I was really proud of you there.

The next glitch, and let's call this a learning experience, came when we tackled Rob and stuffed a chloroform-dipped handkerchief in his face, only to discover that what Heather had acquired for us was almond-flavored Italian syrup from his coffee shop. Now this is one area I'd really like us all to learn from. One of the people who needs to learn from the experience is me, clearly. I need to learn that when Heather brings me a bottle of something that he insists is chloroform, I need to test it to make sure it really is chloroform. I should also do my research, because I was sure that chloroform smelled like almonds, but it turns out that's cyanide.

Thank you, cC-5. Wikipedia *would* be a good resource for that . . . So

235

those are the lessons I should take away. What lessons should everyone else take away? Specifically, what lessons should Heather take away?

Never mind. Heather and I are going to discuss this later. The next learning moment was when Lola and the burlesque troupe tried to distract Rob from choking on almond syrup by launching into a striptease, which instead made Heather faint. But as it turned out, none of these problems was important in the greater scheme of things, because that was when Rob revealed that he was actually bB-1, invasion commander of bB Company, and he called in his army of soldier drones . . . That was when we may have panicked a bit.

People, we really should have stayed and attempted communication with bB Company.

No, really, listen. I know they can be scary, especially in attack mode, but they are fellow pods, after all. Technically speaking, we're all in this together. Much as we'd like this to be a planet of C pods, and much as they'd like it to be a planet of B pods, it's not as if compromise is impossible, right? They probably wouldn't have eaten us once they calmed down.

By the way, cC-3, I'm sorry for leaving Richmond behind. He was just standing there gawking—you know, like he'd never seen an army of pod-born zombies drenched in green synaptic syrup lurching down a produce aisle—and I couldn't drag him away. In the end, he wasn't a bad guy, for someone who wasn't a pod.

So here we are, and I really am the worst invasion commander ever spored from the homeworld. I don't blame the rest of you. You did what you could. This is all on me . . . Me and this stupid planet.

No, cC-5. Thank you, but I really don't want a gift. I don't feel like I deserve a gift right now . . . What is that?

A salad. You brought me a salad.

Oh, a kohlrabi salad. What is with you and kohlrabi?

Look, maybe we should get some sleep and in the morning this will have turned out to be a very bad dr—

Richmond, for heaven's sake, is that you? What on earth are you dragging behind you?

Richmond, that's Rob the assistant manager.

You killed Rob the assistant manager? With a vegetable peeler. That's . . . a vegetable peeler, huh? Wow.

Well, no, you're quite right. You didn't kill Rob the assistant manager. You killed the alien invader who killed Rob the assistant manager. And when you killed him, of course, it immobilized his drones.

That's one of my fellow invasion commanders you just murdered, you know. One of our people . . . Richmond, you weird little human, I could kiss you.

All right, everybody, new plan. The rest of bB Company has to be somewhere in the city. We'll spore into Rob, as planned, except we'll be using his body to infiltrate bB Company. I estimate we can take over their squadron by Labor Day.

We may not be able to make much headway with humans, but we can show those smug know-it-alls from the next nest. Am I right?

Exactly! Everybody give Richmond a hand.

Now who wants salad?

About the Author

SHAENON K. GARRITY is an award-winning cartoonist best known for the webcomics *Narbonic* and *Skin Horse*. Her prose fiction has appeared in *Strange Horizons, Lightspeed, Escape Pod*, and *Daily Science Fiction*. She works as a manga editor for VIZ Media and teaches at the Academy of Art University in San Francisco. Her writing on comics appears regularly in the *Comics Journal* and on Anime News Network. She lives in Berkeley with two birds, a baby, and a man.

Shaenon on Writing
The Invasion Commander's
Motion for New Business

The Button-Down Mind of Bob Newhart. The core concept of this story was "*Invasion of the Body Snatchers* as a Bob Newhart routine." I assume this made sense to me when I started writing, although now I can't remember why. But Newhart's dishcloth-dry comedy has been a great influence on me, just as it has been on countless humor writers. He's cool because he's not trying to be cool, and funny because he doesn't see the joke in anything, and we all wish we had that much style.

I Married a Monster from Outer Space. There are a lot of great movies about body-snatching alien pod people, really more than there should be. From the two best versions of *The Thing* (Howard Hawks's and John Carpenter's) to the two best versions of *Invasion of the Body Snatchers* (1950s' pods in trucks and 1970s' hobo-dog hybrids), filmmakers have tapped a rich vein of sci-fi paranoia and goopy special effects. Then there's this little B picture from 1958, which I like for tackling, as directly as a 1950s' movie can, the concern that alien replicants are probably terrible in bed. The aliens are on Earth to repopulate their planet, but they spend most of their time drinking and griping about having to wear human bodies and live in the suburbs. Also, excellent title.

Alan Mendelsohn, the Boy from Mars. Daniel Pinkwater is one of my lifelong-favorite writers, and I especially like the way he finds mundanity in the fantastic. In *Alan Mendelsohn*, two boys develop telekinetic powers and learn to transport themselves to an alternate universe—and, frankly, it's really boring over there. Some days it doesn't pay to leave Chicago.

The Comic Book Guide to the Mission. I admit I'm partial because I drew a map for it, but this anthology of comics about San Francisco's Mission District is an appropriately eclectic slice of the neighborhood where *The Invasion Commander's Motion for New Business* ostensibly takes place. In a story composed of a series of harried monologues, there isn't much room for vivid descriptions of setting, but I like to think the invasion force is meeting at the It's Tops diner on Market Street, identifiable by the "AWΣSOME HOT CAKES" sign over the door.

Rainbow Grocery in San Francisco. That place has bring-your-own-bottle bulk olive oil. This should be a thing everywhere.

ANN ARBOR VENUS WALKS INTO A BAR

KENZIE ALLEN

I'm sure there's an appropriate cocktail
for every breakup. I've run out on so many
I've run out of business cards for the rebounds.
Anything can happen. Every drink here named
for some type of bruise, lateral or oblique,
with or without basil, and they even muddle
the cherry skins. Vulcan slides a brewski
down the lacquer, collecting icicles stiff
for my upper lip. The doorway is so narrow
you must sidle in next to me like you love
the person you're with. *What's the catch?*
There's never enough of too much light,
never a stained-glass shade I didn't stage
a crush on, and *what are we doing here,*
exactly? Let's not pretend the setting matters
enough to write about winter. This is Pamina's
nuclear bunker, strung up with leftover
pumpkin lights (just to spread some cheer), and
even if I'm close—my tongue an errant antenna,

groping your lobes, seeking nectar, or knives—
it's getting cramped in here. The end times
are coming, and I'm ready. I'm ready, almost.

About the Author

KENZIE ALLEN is a Zell Fellow in poetry at the University of Michigan's Helen Zell Writers' Program (MFA 2014), and a descendant of the Oneida Tribe of Indians of Wisconsin. She is at work on her first manuscript of poetry, a chapbook of Texas poems, and a memoir about blood quantum. Her poems have previously appeared in *Sonora Review*, the *Iowa Review*, and *Word Riot*. Kenzie is also a classically trained lyric soprano, a digital illustrator and UI/UX maven, and a devotee of the desert.

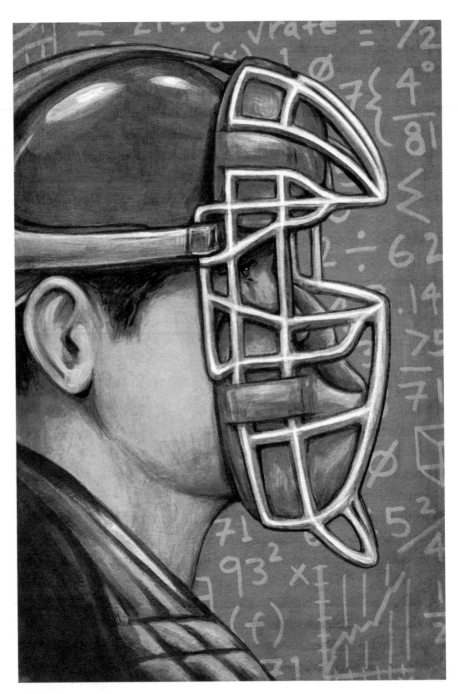

Keith Carter © 2014

THE CUTOFF MAN

CHAD BENSON

Engelmann was the catcher, the smartest in the league, but the information-storing quadrants of his brain were so differently shaped from those of his teammates that his knowledge remained off-limits. He calculated statistics for each facet of the game that defied transcription, obscure enough to baffle a competent Newtonian, much less some utility infielder who'd dropped out of the ninth grade. Even if Engelmann had possessed the ability to communicate in more than grunts (which, believe me, he did not), it would have been impossible for anyone else to grasp firsthand the data that made him so valuable.

Fortunately, Engelmann's own private mastery turned out to be more than sufficient. He informed each of the ten thousand tiny decisions required of a catcher during a ball game with reams of information from his deepest synaptic catacombs. The advantage he gave his pitchers over opposing hitters, the knack for calling a changeup or a slow curve when the batter was thinking fastball all the way, was uncanny. It drove Engelmann's backup, Howard Beechy, to envious grumbling, and it astounded the team's manager, Happy Truman, who'd once fancied himself to be the league's premier reservoir of baseball esoterica.

It flat-out spooked the team's twin aces, Marty and Lenny Penobscot, and the Penobscots were not easily spooked. They were tall and broad men, well proportioned, boarding school–educated. They did Ouija and Pilates and cavorted with scarved women in political exile from Sudan and Cuba. They had witnessed, at the age of nine in a Chicago nightclub, the mob-related stabbings of their mother and father.

The Penobscots had also been born just barely Siamese, joined by a tiny isthmus of arm skin that required a quick postpartum snip. No more than a solitary drop of rich red blood had been shed that morning, but the wounds never fully healed. Each brother retained a nubby tab of scar tissue that jutted forth from his pitching elbow.

Early in their careers, a frustrated opposing manager who'd suffered mimeographed defeats to the hard-throwing left- and right-handed brothers had petitioned the league, insisting that the garbanzo-sized peduncles on the Penobscots' throwing arms created just enough distraction to tangle up his batters. He declared this to be an unfair practice and argued that for the sport to remain credible, the commissioner had no choice but to order those nubs removed in what he could only imagine would be a supersimple procedure, requiring dummy-proof amounts of anesthesia.

The commissioner, however, dismissed the motion, citing various civil rights and disability acts, leaning unnecessarily on an interstate commerce clause, and suggesting through wryly tilted bifocals that the manager might be suffering from a scathing -*itis* of the sour-grape varietal. Perhaps, said the commissioner, this manager's stingy team owner ought to pony up for some talented young prospects instead of trotting out a squad of rickety veterans who'd faded into ghosts of themselves (which every insider and sportswriter agreed this particular team had a tendency to do). The rest of the league sort of laughed it off, embarrassed, secretly grateful that someone else had at least given it a shot.

Incidentally, you shouldn't expect this to be the kind of story where Marty and Lenny find out who killed their parents. They never did. That's how it happens sometimes.

The issue of the nubs didn't come up again until the incident I want to tell you about, which is something that occurred ten seasons later, when for a few glorious weeks the Penobscots and their teammates achieved a level of baseball perfection only visited upon this earth maybe a handful of times per century. It sent fans and players alike scrambling for Bibles and crystals and Las Vegas bookies to try to make sense of it. Those few weeks were the best I've ever known. They altered the course of my life forever, though now it all feels like something that happened to a different person entirely.

I once asked Engelmann what he thought about those skin bits on Marty's and Lenny's arms. He just rocked his torso and stared at a spot four inches below and to the left of my face, because that's what Engelmann did. Engelmann didn't talk to *nobody*. On occasion, if it was an especially splendid baseball day and something rare or beautiful occurred on the field, he might engage in a few seconds of strong and meaningful eye contact with his catcher's mitt. If you asked him to dinner or nudged him and whistled after a hip-tossing blonde, he was 100 percent brick wall.

But I can guarantee you (and this is one of those stories where you should assume that what I tell you is true) that when the ruling about the Penobscots' nubs came down from the commissioner, Engelmann was a very happy man. He kept buckets of stats in his head about those little skin blobs, and he knew exactly how to make good use of them. Depending on the angle of the sun, the barometer, the whiff of lunch on a batter's breath, Engelmann (I'm certain) could determine the miniscule degree to which those Penobscot skin tags would obscure the trajectory of a tailing fastball, making it harder to hit than even a devastating slider in the dirt (that slider being an obvious Penobscot strength that a lesser catcher would have defaulted to in the same situation).

The rest of the pitching staff (up until that unprecedented run I'm going to recount) was awful, but Engelmann's shrewdness boosted them past their limited talents, and this alone kept the Barons competitive. The Birmingham Barons. Though not the Birmingham you're probably thinking of. We had a dead-armed lefty junkballer named Muddy Alvarado and two guys in their midforties who'd had the famous Tommy John elbow surgery so many times we just called them Tommy and John. If anyone in the lineup could have hit their weight, the Barons might have been something to see. As it stood, each season was a battle to finish in second place rather than third, every game a stinge-fest for the one or two runs that got scored. Unless it was a bad day. If Tommy or John or Muddy couldn't find a rhythm or lost control of their off-speed pitches, then you were looking at a 12–0 shellacking. Sometimes, not even Engelmann could rescue those guys.

Midway through the season that I'm talking about, a decade into the Penobscots' careers, when they'd already reserved their spots in the Hall of Fame but hadn't yet begun to physically decline, an event transpired that changed everything. It caused the whole ball club, for the first time in ages, to beat back superstition and wander into the forbidden territory of hope, to stray from the comforts of mediocrity and consider graspable (in a knock-on-wood sort of way) the possibility of winning a championship.

What happened that day was this: Pudge Morrison—aging veteran left fielder who'd failed to imagine his way into life after baseball and returned for too many twilight seasons, diluting and ruining what could have been a respectable set of career statistics—struck out to end the game. Again. All season long he'd been struggling worse than ever, and on this day he'd failed to drive home a rare Baron base runner who'd been hit by a pitch, stolen second base, and advanced to third on a dribbly ground ball. Pudge had never been a great hitter, even in his prime, but now in middle age he'd turned to unadulterated dogshit. His contribution to the Barons consisted merely of adequate defense in left field. Even his locker room presence, once garrulous and fun-loving, had deteriorated into a sullen and contagious funk.

Pudge's wife and three daughters lived way out in San Diego. He was getting old and lonely climbing the dugout stairs with aching knees, sleeping in a rented downtown efficiency, trying to save money for a retirement that scared him even worse than striking out every night. It was all these years on the road that constituted his real life: drinking on trains, kicking up dust, girls in hotels. Not some suburban idyll in Southern California with a too-smart trophy wife who'd already lost her glint. The game might be getting harder to enjoy, but at least he was still suiting up every night.

So after ending the game with a strikeout for the who-knows-how-many-th time (Engelmann probably knew, actually), Pudge Morrison accepted truly sincere condolences (not the masked, passive-aggressive kind) from Buck Hodge, Richard Ratigan, and Sean O'Malley. These three, along with Hitsui Takahashi—the six-foot-eight Japanese import who played first base—made up the Barons' infield, a close-knit group of chatterboxes who popped gum and exchanged knock-knock jokes while fielding the between-inning grounders that Takahashi delivered with robotic grace. When Pudge Morrison struck out to end a game, they legitimately felt bad for him.

There is, among baseball players, if nothing else, tremendous empathy. It's due to the sharing of so much common failure. Even the most legendary hitters get on base less than half the time, and the best teams win maybe two of every three games. It seemed to Pudge that Takahashi, too, was genuine with his encouragement, but this was harder to figure. Takahashi spoke through a translator, who also happened to be a willowy six-foot redheaded blast furnace, distracting enough when she wasn't even talking, much less reproducing a subtle Japanese undertone or an unspoken Japanese sentiment. (Her name was Delilah. In addition to being willowy, she was also a Rhodes Scholar and spoke some Mandarin to go along with the Japanese. I mean, she was really something.)

And so after the strikeout, after the hangdog toss of the helmet and the ripping of Velcro batting-glove straps and the sulk off the field down the corridor to his clubhouse locker with the padded folding chair, after the stripping down to jockstrap and socks and dangling golden crucifix, Pudge Morrison looked up from the scarred relief map of his knees and saw one thing he expected to see and one thing he did not.

The thing he expected to see was three female reporters shoving microphones in his face, asking how it felt to end yet another game on a humiliating note when his teammates so often rose to the challenge and at times performed almost brilliantly. To this, he was accustomed. Years earlier, when women had gained access to the locker room through freedom-of-equal-employment stuff, guys had responded by getting naked more than usual and clandestinely chubbing themselves up, at first in flagrant protest and then from insecurity's onset. A few major stars in the league actually eschewed the warm glow of media attention due to concerns about their endowments while lengthier journeymen and career benchwarmers chatted freely from wide stances about games they hadn't even played in. Pudge fell somewhere in between, though at this stage in his career he no longer cared much about who sized up his duffel bag. His desire to avoid the reporters was rooted in a different embarrassment, the one where he clearly didn't deserve to be in the starting lineup.

Owing to some fealty that persisted solely in the most sentimental and gentlemanly of American sports, Happy Truman kept Pudge out there in left field night after night, batting at the bottom of the order, ostensibly for defense. But defense didn't win ball games. The truth was, Pudge and Happy went back a long way together, all the way to the Texas League, and that meant something in baseball. Even more than winning, in some cases, especially if the chances of your team winning weren't great to begin with. Happy was the grumpiest son of a barn cat you ever met, but don't go thinking this is some kind of Dickens tale. Happy was just a nickname. Grumpy guys get called Happy all the time in baseball.

And so Pudge Morrison expected to see those reporters with their microphones asking questions and checking out his junk. As luck would have it, his was hanging pretty loose and attractive that evening, and though he officially didn't care, it would be foolish to pretend this didn't hearten him a bit.

But the thing Pudge did not expect to see, the thing that kicked off this entire mystical turnaround the Barons were about to experience, was a pale little girl, about ten years old, in a stiff red dress pulled tight at the waist by a shiny black belt. That dress looked like a red bow tie turned on its side. She wore a single braided ebony pigtail that extended straight out from the left side of her head like an Allen wrench. It didn't appear that the second pigtail had come undone out of sloppiness or neglect. In fact, it was pretty clear there had never been a second pigtail. The girl looked perfectly nourished and cared-for.

Pudge Morrison was the first to see her, but he was not the first to speak. From the far side of the locker room, someone angrily called out to ask who'd brought the little girl, who'd brought their kid in the clubhouse for godsakes? The initial assumption was that she must belong to one of the female reporters, but all the reporters shook their heads and made faces that said, "Don't look at me, I don't even want one." Next, all the infielders and outfielders and starters and relievers turned to each other with raised eyebrows, wondering who'd let their admittedly adorable daughter into the clubhouse. It was bad enough that they had to commingle with lady reporters appraising their roots on top of their performances, but a line had to be drawn at little kids, who probably weren't yet covered by fair-employment equal-access legislation and surely deserved a few more years' protection from life's male grotesqueries.

The girl stood still in the middle of the locker room, hands at her sides, looking around expectantly, a little nervous but not afraid, as though searching for someone she was ten minutes early to meet. All the players came to their senses and interrupted the whodunit vibe to cover their crotches with whatever material was handy: mitts, hats, folding chairs, Scientology pamphlets.

By the time all fourteen position players and eleven pitchers and six coaches and nine female reporters and a trainer and a guru and a willowy redheaded translator (who read Tacitus just for kicks) made it clear they had no idea who this girl belonged to, it was quiet enough to hear Engelmann's lips moving as he gently rocked on his hinges and committed the day's statistics to memory.

Calls were made and messages sent. The girl didn't talk, didn't respond to questions, didn't cry, didn't let on to who she was. Outside in the ballpark, though the bleachers were drained of all but a few autograph-seeking fans, the PA announcer put the word out to the stadium that a little girl was missing her mother. Nobody knew what to do. It was like we had another Engelmann on our hands, but smaller and less valuable. An hour passed. Two. Exasperation set in.

The Barons were scheduled to board a flight to Portland that night (not the Portland you're thinking of, probably) and with the police unable to take the girl into custody (due to all those controversial missing-person laws) and the reporters insistent that something had to be done and second and third phone calls made to hospitals and news stations by Marketing and Communications so that a mother would know for sure the girl was safely aboard the Barons' jet if she sought her out via those channels, Happy Truman finally growled, "Aw, hell, we got a schedule to keep," and carried the girl on the bus.

I know that sounds far-fetched. That we just up and loaded the girl onto a bus full of spitting, scratching ballplayers when she was clearly lost from home. But remember that the Barons were a bunch of twentysomething guys (and a few crotchety vets) with their minds on baseball and beer and those slits up the backs of tight linen skirts—anything except how to deal with a lost child. If they'd wanted that sort of job, they would have assumed responsibility for their own kids.

Plus, our spirits were already taxed to the limit. We had the weight of discerning and sometimes hateful crowds on our shoulders. Performance anxiety. The thing with the female reporters always tipping their eyes toward our cocks while we tried to explain away four consecutive losses. None of us had much energy to spare. It was easier to hope that someone else would handle it.

That's what the skipper of the team is there for. He grabs the bull and the buck stops there. The whole locker room (including the doting reporters, who immediately understood that coursing estrogen had written checks for the girl's caretaking that none of their ambitious lifestyles could cash) breathed this massive whoosh of relief, and we all filed onto the bus. Happy put on his best grandfather act and handed the girl a sandwich and asked if she'd like to come on a plane ride, if she'd like to stay with us until we found her parents. He looked uneasy, but he did what he had to.

The girl rode next to him and chewed a bit of the sandwich (never really swallowing), staring forward, smiling a little once in a while and looking at her toes, then staring forward again. She maintained an unnervingly erect posture and didn't seem the least bit worried. She dangled her legs off the seat and swung them to and fro, like any kid would.

Next night, we clobbered Portland, 13–1. The girl sat in the dugout with the team and never left Happy's side, even when he sprinted onto the field to argue a close call with the umpire in the third inning, kicking up dirt with his cleats. Tommy pitched a gem of a game, only gave up three hits and one run. Engelmann threw out two base runners at second. The bats were on fire, and even old Pudge Morrison banged a double off the wall in right center that scored two runs.

Night after that? Walloped Portland again. Last game of the series on Wednesday afternoon? You guessed it. Another bloodbath in favor of the good guys. So there went any misgivings about swooping a mysterious orphan up into our traveling road show like some goldfish we'd won at the fair. You can imagine how the Barons ignored the sad weirdness of nobody coming to look for the girl, how victory served as grist for denial. Fan-frigging-tastic, the players said. Keep that little charmer in tow. Hitsui Takahashi's translator (who used a pen to solve those bridge problems next to the horoscopes in the paper) bought her a new dress and tried to comb her hair, but still that pigtail stuck out like an arrow. After Portland came Columbus (not the Columbus you're probably thinking of), and the Barons put on another dazzling display. The Penobscots threw back-to-back shutouts, and Engelmann hit eight consecutive singles to the exact same part of the field. He'd apparently rigged that labyrinth in his noggin to make additional room for some hitting data, upgraded his brain with an extra chunk of RAM.

After the Barons ticked off eleven wins in a row, everyone stopped asking where the girl had come from. Baseball players are medievally superstitious, and when things are going well, you neither alter the arrangement nor speak its name. You eat the same breakfast with the same fork pocketed from Elias Brothers, following the same counterclockwise path around the dish. You only chew the second piece of gum from each pack. You don't wash your stirrups. And if a little girl in a red dress with a pigtail wanders into your clubhouse and you subsequently embark on a double-digit winning streak, you most certainly do not try to find that girl's parents or muse out loud about what the heck's happening. What you do is you put on your spikes and jog out to left field and bounce there on the balls of your feet and shag high flies until the end of the inning when it's time to trot in for some cuts, and then you pick up your bat and swing at the ball and maybe you run to first base but soon you're back in left to do it all over again. No need to try to throw the runner out from the warning track. Just hit the cutoff man and let him make the relay. One task after the next. Each successive moment becomes its own entire universe. Don't get ahead of yourself. One at a time. Ninety-four percent of your consciousness suspended.

Two-thirds of the way through the season, the Barons found themselves one game out of first place. In the month of July they'd gone 23–4. If the arms and bats and luck held up, they'd go on to win the division and be favored to take the whole shebang come championship time. We all felt good. Even Happy Truman. He embraced his grandfatherly role, spoiled the girl with Cracker Jack and cotton candy and expensive kiddie manicures. The sun rose and set at just the right times for everyone to get enough sleep. The food was expertly cooked. The air oozed with that warm-bath quality that makes a summer night feel like the perfect opportunity to ignore time's passage and live perfectly still among fireflies and crickets and damp green grass, richly blended infield dirt raked free of pebbles, and the crippling beauty of two chalked foul lines. That summer felt like the dawn of Creation for the Birmingham Barons. Pure paradise.

As the season crested over Labor Day and headed toward the playoffs, Pudge Morrison began to contemplate his family life while riding on buses, drinking in hotel rooms, sitting on restaurant bathroom toilets. With so much still on the line, it was bad form to think about anything other than hitting and catching, but he was giddy with victory and granted himself the indulgence.

Pudge had been given a rare second chance. If he'd been injured at twenty-eight and forced to retire, sleeping under the same roof each night with his wife and kids might have been bearable. His existence could have been something like that of a fierce king wounded in battle during his physical prime. The subsequent failures (running a car dealership into the ground, embarrassing sitcom cameos, handcrafting leaky and porous kayaks that sank like barbells) would have been easily forgiven as the eccentricities of a retired warrior. People would have accepted the fact that Pudge was no businessman or actor, but my goodness, what a damned fine ballplayer.

But Pudge had not gone out on top. He'd lingered and languored and declined in public. Now, at thirty-five, deterioration and failure had poisoned the fruits of his sole talent, rendering his youthful accomplishments moot. To his wife and kids, Pudge Morrison was a screech of the tires that made them flinch, dreading the unsightly crash to come. If he retired with a fizzle at the end of another lackluster season, the world would believe that Pudge had been driven from the game and put out to pasture. Deposed kings didn't get to while away their graying years as charming dilettantes. They became the fools of their own courts. Pudge could sense it in the way his family looked at him, the two blonde daughters and the one brunette, the diabetic pet chinchillas and the day-trading gardener, the wife who tactfully refrained from asking about life on the road but who also might never have liked him.

All that would change if this streak kept up and he retired on the heels of a championship season, a great diamond ring all aflash on his knuckle. He could play thrice-weekly golf and not take flack for the clogged-up gutters, because, after all, he was a world champion, who'd labored many years and finally acquired the ultimate prize in his field. His wife would shake her head, bemused on the phone, and say to her friends things like "What can you do," and "You know what they say about an old ballplayer." That was a life he could handle.

During the first home stand of September, Pudge went five for thirteen against Salem and made a diving catch in left center that saved a run and secured another victory for either Tommy or John (I forget which). The girl adopted the customs of the rally and wore the same red dress each game, laundered by Delilah, who kept the new dress she'd bought in her luggage, just in case, next to the Tacitus. The girl sat in the same spot in the dugout, at the center of the bench, next to Happy Truman, with her socks pulled up and her feet dangling. Nobody called or claimed her, not even falsely, and though each player had surely tinkered with his own version of an origin myth, these were never discussed out loud.

As Pudge jogged back to the dugout following his second home run of the Salem series, he noticed the girl gazing distractedly into the upper deck and making, for the first time since she'd arrived, a kind of disconcerted squinting face. Not once in the six weeks since her arrival had the girl said a word or expressed dissatisfaction, but this look she now gave was not of her previous arsenal. Then it disappeared, and she twisted her neck just slightly to look him directly in the eye, which is another thing she'd never done. The gesture opened her eye sockets and created a hall-of-mirrors effect. Where Pudge faced down a disorienting row of thousands of nested images of the girl and himself, himself and the girl, stretching on through her eyeholes into a distant otherness of time and space that his brain couldn't fathom. It lasted only a fraction of a heartbeat, but right there Pudge knew exactly what the story was. Not a doubt to be had. Sitting in the Birmingham Barons' very own dugout, dressed up in sheep's clothing if he'd ever seen such, was bad luck itself.

A shudder ran down through Pudge's shoulders and into the tight cords of his hamstrings and calves, escaping through his toes to skitter off into the subterranean dampness from whence such shivers are issued. Pudge was not then nor had he ever been a spiritual man, but he'd played baseball long enough to understand about Fortune and the universe. If things were going too well, in defiance of logic, for no good reason, it meant the pendulum was gearing for a nasty return trip. This highly pinchable and unexplained good-luck girl was nothing of the sort. She'd arrived to swap victories with the Barons for a spiritual debt to be named later. Who knew what demand she'd make when the time came? Pudge took off his batting gloves and helmet and grabbed his mitt. He accidentally offered a high five to Engelmann, which was always awkward. He drained a paper Gatorade cup and stretched his neck and looked down the bench to where the girl sat next to Happy Truman, just waiting to turn on them. He shrugged. They were winning 4–1. It was a beautiful fall evening with plenty of summer still touching the air. What the hell difference did it make how they got their wins?

Three hours after Pudge's realization—which didn't stop him from sending another booming sacrifice fly into right field that scored a run—he gathered with the rest of the team around Hitsui Takahashi and Delilah on the plane from Salem to Springfield (yes, *that* Springfield). Lenny Penobscot's performance on the mound that night had been so nasty, his stuff so wicked and brutal, that the rest of the team could take it no longer. Someone had to ask. We all dispensed with protocol and began pestering our Buddhist teammate for some framework by which to better understand the elevated plane the Penobscots had reached during this recent streak of shutout masterpieces. The twins themselves slept soundly with smiles on their faces a few rows up in reclined seats. The little girl had taken to riding in front with the pilots, which allowed everyone else to relax a little bit.

"Where the body intrudes," Delilah translated for Hitsui Takahashi, "the mind precludes." It was difficult for Pudge to hear Delilah say the word "body" without subsequently regarding hers. He fought through the impulse and caught up with her a few seconds later.

"Hold up," said Pudge. "Is that really how he said it?"

Takahashi nodded, as though he'd understood and approved of what his translator had just said. In truth, what this indicated was not that he understood English but rather that his confidence in Delilah was supreme, due to she'd been a Rhodes Scholar and worked those problems in pen and so forth. "The rhymes are slightly different in Japanese," she admitted. "But I feel I've preserved the meaning."

"What about . . . ?" Muddy Alvarado gestured as lightly as possible with his no-longer-dead left arm toward the front of the airplane. He made a face that suggested what he wanted to say but couldn't say, which was along the lines of, "What about—you know—the *nameless* one? What does your Buddhist knowledge make of her?"

This was borderline treachery. Unlike in the theater—where a taboo phrase can be euphemized by offering hopes of a broken limb—in baseball, any reference whatsoever to the unspeakable (an in-progress no-hitter, a batting streak, a tendency to get beaned by a pitcher you knew you couldn't hit) was a blatant infraction. But the Barons were all so privately curious that once Muddy had broken the seal, we all hung around to catch a whiff of what followed.

Delilah directed a different set of hand and facial gestures toward Hitsui, which I guess was her way of translating Muddy's American body language into Japanese. She was dressed in the green pantsuit I loved so much, the one that pulled tight across her hips and outlined a perfect freckled V of exposed, flattish chest.

Hitsui nodded, again, understanding, and I was struck by how much knowledge resided in that slight, simple gesture. I meant to remark on this, but just as Hitsui was about to speak to Delilah, the plane hit a rough patch that sent bags tumbling from overhead compartments and tossed unbuckled ballplayers into the aisle. The lights flickered. The floor dropped and swooped up to meet us. Then it was still again.

Everyone, even Hitsui, looked horrified. We gathered ourselves together and straightened our ties and pants and returned the luggage to where it belonged. No one spoke for the rest of the flight. It had nothing to do with gravitas or fearing for our lives. Everyone knew we'd broken a rule and it was all going to end. We'd blown it. Who was to blame? Was it Muddy, for making that face? Delilah, for translating it? All of us for sitting idly by? Even Engelmann, to my mind at least, seemed to twitch nervously just a little bit in the upper part of his right cheek as he stared into the seatback in front of him.

The plane landed in Springfield without incident, and the Barons glumly disembarked. The next day, as expected, the girl was gone. No one could say when it happened. She rode with the team to the hotel, showed up for the team meal, was there in the clubhouse while players taped their wrists and soaked their aching limbs in cold whirlpools. But when we took the field and looked back over our shoulders, Happy Truman sat by himself in the dugout. I think we all secretly hoped she was in the bathroom or something, but then we'd never known her to use the bathroom. Good old denial kept us from losing our composure, but it didn't stop us from losing the game. Marty Penobscot couldn't find his pinpoint control and walked eight guys in six innings, gave up nine runs. Some knuckleballer with an 8–10 record and a 5.29 ERA held us to three hits and no runs. The ball looked like a drunken mosquito flying toward me. I never had a prayer of hitting it.

The flight home, again, was silent. In a way, the girl's disappearance had broken a tension that had begun to feel unbearable. The Barons had understood the rules. We'd known this winning couldn't go on indefinitely and that no lucky streak or strange orphan was permanent. In the same way the anticipation is worse than the actual blow when you offer your debtor a free punch to the face and you're standing there waiting for it, so is Fortune's actual reversal less agonizing than the dread of its arrival.

Eventually, the spell broke. Various wisecracks and jokes found their legs and a steady outburst of chatter filled the plane. We'd been freed from the constraints of a superstitious vigil, but it wasn't a full or authentic relief. The Barons had made a crucial mistake and allowed themselves to peek too far down the road, to wonder if maybe just this once the universe would cut them a break, turn a blind eye, allow them a disproportionate share of the glory. They'd fallen into the trap of anticipating the future, of expanding their minds to occupy more than one moment. They'd let themselves hope. And what better recipe for disappointment?

We lost three in a row at home to Ontario and then two out of three to Washington. Hitsui Takahashi took it better than anyone. Muddy Alvarado and Howard Beechy (who never even played) found it impossible to maintain the vaguest approximation of sobriety. You couldn't really call what Engelmann did "taking it well," because Engelmann didn't take it at all. He just plodded along, leaning on his statistics, batting an even .250 and calling for all the right pitches, even when Tommy and John and Muddy (and even the Penobscots) failed to properly execute them. Happy Truman went back to compulsively munching oyster crackers, carefully cracking them in half with his incisors and mashing them up with his tongue. Fans began to boo. And in the hours following yet another loss, on a Tuesday night, having been once again prodded with unforgiving microphones while his genitals shriveled, Pudge Morrison experienced his first fully realized nervous breakdown.

If his teammates had misstepped by permitting themselves unwise optimism, Pudge had fallen from the roof. Now, doubled over on the floor, he shook his head as though trying to rid himself of a batting helmet without using his hands. He banged his knees and elbows against the wall. He dry-heaved and spat and cursed. A giant worm of doubt had burrowed deep into him, and no contortion or spasm would expel it. Near dawn of the next day, raw-throated and five pounds lighter, he finally exhausted himself and slipped into feverish stillness.

Pudge had banked his entire psychic solvency on the winning of a championship. Monumental success was supposed to excuse and underwrite his ensuing retirement, afford him some dignity when life shifted from fifth gear to first. Now he faced down the prospect of a life's second half filled with memories of prolonged failure at the one thing he'd ever tried to do. None of the myriad joys he'd experienced would travel those final miles alongside him. The obvious solution was to pull himself together and believe they could win without the girl. The easier solution was unthinkable and tempting.

The first week of October saw the Barons maintaining a slim one-game lead in their division with a single game left to play. Their hot streak had been so hot that even the late-season collapse following the girl's disappearance hadn't completely ruined their record. If they won the final game against Portland, they would at least advance to the play-offs. If they lost, it was time to go home, throw away all those phone numbers with strange area codes, and dig out the swimming trunks and golf clubs.

Baseball is a game of momentum, and on the day of the face-off with Portland, the Barons had none. Happy Truman needed a crowbar to get his players up off the clubhouse seats and onto the field. Batting practice was drudgery. The infield trio of Ratigan, O'Malley, and Hodge fielded warm-up ground balls with the enthusiasm of men convicted to hang for petty crimes. At times, they didn't bother to field the ground balls at all but just stood there dejected with their mitts on their hips, watching them roll by, no longer seeing the point of it.

In the clubhouse after warm-ups, Happy Truman told Lenny Penobscot he was pitching, even though it wasn't his turn in the rotation and he was shitfaced drunk from mixing white wine with lunch. Lenny slouched down next to Engelmann, and Engelmann did something I'd never seen him do before. He pointed. With his finger. Unmistakably. At the tiny bit of skin protruding from Lenny's left elbow. Lenny frowned, puzzled. Engelmann then used that same finger, which had never meant anything but "Throw a fastball," to describe an arc that began at his left knee and finished, unmistakably, with a swipe across the exposed part of his throat. Then he returned to the universe of himself.

The message was clear: lose the nub.

Lenny continued to nod, understanding, terrified, not the least bit wise looking. I handed him a pair of toenail clippers and he carried them toward the bathroom stalls, where he could be alone. Lenny, like all of us, was willing to do whatever it took. What nobody knew was whether Engelmann had made the call based on cold fronts and batting averages and the migration patterns of a local butterfly or if even he had succumbed to the last-ditch and desperate. We all heard a snip, the sharp exhalation of breath, then a sigh. Delilah found a Band-Aid, but Engelmann shook his head no and she stuffed it back into her purse. We pretended not to hear Lenny's vomit slapping against the tile floor of the shower room. None of us knew what to say to him. He only bled for a second.

I hadn't slept, shaved, or showered in the previous twenty-four hours. The night terrors had plagued me all week, so grisly that I figured I was paying the entire team's psychic debt to the little brat in the red dress. Screeching bottle rockets and hydraulic pistons tortured my skull. I didn't know whether I could drag myself out there. If you'd seen me, you would have said, "Pudge, you're a mess."

I don't believe I'll ever get that low again. I've been through hard times and good, but that was easily the worst. Some nights, I still find comfort in believing that everything since has been an improvement. Which isn't to say that Lenny's amputation sparked a rally and we won that day against Portland. Or that we went on to win a championship and I caught a flight back to Franny and the kids and the rodents in San Diego to put myself out to stud, or that I lived a long and prosperous retirement. Then again, it's also not to say that those things didn't happen. What I mean to describe is a shifting of focus, a realization that in the relationship between high and low there's a little of each in the other. Regardless of what came next, my lowness of spirit that day couldn't possibly have gotten any lower, and that's something you can't understand until you've felt it. But did it resolve? Did I rise up and achieve grand heights or simply a less low lowness? The answer is: it depends on how you view it.

Following the impromptu surgery, in the minutes before we took the field for the do-or-die showdown with Portland, we sat around the clubhouse quietly fearing a crushing disappointment. We forced ourselves not to hope that Lenny would return to form after clipping his bump. We prayed that we might unshoulder this burden and undo the entire season, return to bland mediocrity, link off to address our own private nauseas. After watching Lenny mime a few inconclusive warm-up tosses in front of the mirror, I turned to see all six feet eight inches of Hitsui Takahashi glaring down at me, silent, as though he were marveling at the smallness of an ant.

I said, "How do you do it, Takahashi-san? How do you keep so cool?"

Hitsui's was a stony demeanor, though not without its compassionate edges. Before he'd heard the full translation, I could in his face see that he understood me, even cared about me. The notion that he and I and the rest of the Barons were somehow related, brothers not just in arms but in spirit or blood, didn't seem too far-fetched. It was very moving. Then he spoke.

"Yesterday she was here," Delilah translated. "Today she is gone. It is the same thing."

I let that sink in for a moment. I said, "Could you maybe elucidate?"

I've seen lots of baseball players make the sign of the cross when they hit a home run. Hitsui was the first I'd ever known to make a yin-yang with his hands, curling the fingers of one into the fingers of the other with one palm facing toward the ground and one toward the sky. He did this now and spoke for a long time, calmly, but with flecks of spittle escaping his mouth. When he'd finished, Delilah thought for a moment. Then she translated.

"Yesterday she was here," she said. "Today she is gone. It is the same thing."

I made eyebrows at her. She shrugged.

"In Japanese, there are many ways to say this."

Hitsui grinned and spoke again. Delilah watched him carefully and once more began to translate.

"Yesterday she was here—"

"Alright, enough," I said. "I got it." But I didn't. I didn't get it at all. "Can't you ask him to say something else? Something Buddhist? This isn't helping."

Delilah reached out and touched me very softly on the shoulder. I felt a shock run through me. It was as though she'd translated Hitsui Takahashi's words into physical contact. I immediately felt ashamed for not at first understanding. Then I lightened and forgot the ache in my knees. The day made sense in a way that I couldn't explain.

"What you have to do," Delilah said, cutting off Hitsui before he had a chance to respond, "is tell yourself the right kind of story. In English, there's no good way to explain this. The story was a cakewalk when she was here. The one for today will be harder. Tomorrow's is going to be the worst. But the girl means nothing. She never did. And so she means everything."

With a nurse's tenderness she tapped me on the head, as though that was where the stories came from. We nodded together like three wise people who understood they didn't know anything. Then Hitsui Takahashi smacked me hard on the rump and barked like a dog, which he took to be an American jock thing even though it wasn't. Happy Truman clapped his hands twice. The team stood up, and we all headed through the tunnel to the field.

During the first inning, it appeared that Lenny's nub-ectomy had brought him back to life. He retired the side one-two-three. In the second, he gave up a hit and a walk but didn't surrender any runs. But by the fifth, Portland started doing damage, and it was clear that we were all on our own out there. Maybe Engelmann had been wrong. Or maybe things would have been even worse if he hadn't taken action. There was no way to know. I guess that's always the case.

We didn't beat Portland that day and we didn't go to the play-offs and we didn't win a championship. But I also didn't disgrace myself. *We* didn't disgrace *ourselves*. In the end, Lenny pitched pretty well but not his best and we all quit thinking about the girl with the pigtail. I went one for four and got robbed of a double when Portland's third baseman made a leaping grab. We lost 4–2, but we played pretty good. I no longer worried about making an error in left field at the worst possible moment or striking out swinging or returning to a lame existence with a disappointed family in San Diego. I took it one pitch at a time, drank in every burble and swell of applause, paid attention to the gorgeous crack of a leather ball against a wooden bat that had supplied my life's soundtrack for so many years, and in just a few hours, would cease to.

For the first time in years, I didn't feel stretched out wider than myself. I was free from dread, and the next moment arrived untainted and neutral, fresh as a new lover. I never failed to live my way through it. And then I lived through another one. Some moments pleased me more than others. Some moments stank wretchedly. The moment when I poked a single into shallow right that scored our only two runs was an especially nice one. The moment when I got ahead on a three-and-one count but swung over the top of a juicy fastball and grounded out instead of flinging one into the left-center gap was a bummer. But I refused to succumb to the belief that a streak of bummers was coming down the pipe. I reset to zero. I told myself that fear of failure was worse than failure. Which might have been what Delilah was talking about. Or maybe not. Regardless, it worked.

So there it is. Probably not the tale you were after, but it's the only one I know. And like I said, this is not the kind of story where a crime gets solved or Engelmann learns to love. It's not even the kind where you find out exactly who that little girl in the red dress was, or where she came from, though that would be a reasonable expectation. And it definitely isn't the kind of story where good old Pudge Morrison returns home surprised to find that his wife and children have strung up a "Welcome Home, Daddy. You're a Hero!" banner.

The truth is that mine will be a life of plodding through a one-legged marriage with waves of regret crashing frequently over me, devastating at high tide but less so at low. It will depress and be brutal with the occasional reprieve at my daughters' dance recitals and weddings. I'll drink more than I want to and spend time fixing unbroken things in the basement to avoid saying awkward things to my wife. But like Takahashi-san would tell you, none of that stuff is the end of the world. You just do it. Head down. Shoulder to the plow. Like preseason push-ups and suicide wind sprints. You have to be careful not to drop your guard—don't start thinking about everything at once. Remember not to get ahead of yourself. Watch the ball. Forget about swinging for the fences. Let a pitch go by now and then, to see how they're breaking. Another one will always follow. And then another. And another. And then one day they'll stop.

It's really not so terrible.

About the Author

CHAD BENSON grew up outside of Detroit, Michigan, and currently lives in Brooklyn, New York, where he recently completed his first novel. His short stories have appeared in *Portland Review*, the *South Carolina Review*, and the *Collagist*. He received his MFA from New York University.

Brooke Weeber © 2014

OF EQUAL OR LESSER VALUE

KEVIN SKIENA

Tracy is late, again, so far by thirteen minutes. Jeff recognizes the ugliness of his feelings—how he wishes that when she *did* come in late, she were more ashamed of it. What she'll do is fast-walk past the counter to the break room to put away her purse and get her red CVS vest, look at Jeff, smile in her sweet way (it really is a sweet smile, the kind that makes most people forget their bitterness), mouth an apology, and then she's done. How much penance Jeff would like from her he is not sure. On the few occasions when he, himself, is late, he feels a flutter in his heart, something like a hand closing on his heart. He will sweat a little, apologize to everyone, one by one, like a child before a classroom, and feel low for an hour or two.

The door to the manager's office opens, and Alice, the assistant manager, appears with a freshly counted till. She maneuvers between Jeff and the cigarettes to get to Register 1, keys it open, inserts the till.

"Has she called?" Jeff asks, ringing and bagging a box of Kotex pads.

"Nope," Alice says. She opens Register 2's cash drop, the coupon drop, and then the register drawer.

"Have we called her?" he asks.

Alice pretends not to hear him above the jangle of coins. She sighs. "I'll give you a break in forty," she says as the counter door swings closed behind her.

Saying thank you feels too generous, so he says, "Okay." What he thinks is, *Other people get away with things for which I would be more sternly punished.*

It's not that the work is hard. The work is ridiculously easy, and this is part of the problem. It's so easy that he has time to think these things as he goes, about the inadequacy and disappointment of the work itself. (He nudges open a plastic bag, rings up shampoo, mascara, lipstick, and totals them.) They've had part-timers who've struggled with manually entering ten-digit UPC codes. It's an important and rudimentary skill, the ability to accurately type ten digits into a keypad when a bar code fails to scan, and yet . . .

Jeff can even argue the finer points of a coupon's terms with an unhappy customer, which seems like a judo master skill compared to what some of his coworkers do, which is punch in the discount manually to avoid any disagreement. Though there are few things as degrading to Jeff as arguing with a customer about a dollar or fifty cents as if he wants it.

What happens often are things like: Register makes angry beep at coupon. Jeff reads coupon. Before he has even finished, Customer says, "That's for the paper towels," as if Jeff can't read the print or doesn't understand the prominent, glossy picture of paper towels. He continues reading. Customer, who had been standing sort of at ease, comes to attention somewhat, cocking a hip, as if about to argue with someone very dim.

"This is one per customer," Jeff says.

"I have three of them." This is said like it's an argument *in support of.* Jeff thinks, *Do not engage.*

"The first one went through, but I can't accept more than one."

Customer slouches, mouth agape. Posture says either *Come on* or *Are you serious?* Sometimes, these things are said aloud. "Are you serious?"

This question never fails to sink Jeff's mood, because he is both completely serious and so far removed from his own value-appraisal apparatus that he doesn't recognize what's driving his actions. He cannot say, "Yes, I am serious," which would come across as sarcastic (read, combative), so he softens further.

"It's our policy. I'm sorry."

Customer either folds here or, more often, says, "I could leave right now and come back in a half hour or tomorrow and use the same damn coupon over and over as many times as I want, right? So, save me the trip. It's fifty cents."

Customer is right. It's a logistical and logical fault in the system, but there's no way around it. Manually entering three fifty-cent discounts would trigger follow-ups from the store's manager, Ron, which happened the first time Jeff was won over by such logic. Jeff couldn't say to Ron, "I don't remember," because who wouldn't remember the monotony of manually typing in a fifty-cent discount three times? Ron would surely point to the abundance of paper-towel coupons in the coupon drop as well as the single transaction consisting of three paper-towel rolls and the discounts in question. Jeff had explained the customer's argument to Ron, which was awkward—justifying someone else's dollar-fifty policy violation as if the cause were his own.

"The coupon says," Ron had started, pausing to read the coupon. "A coupon is a contract. We've got to go by what the contract says. Someone could walk in with a hundred of these."

"How effective can these paper towels be if you need to buy a hundred of them?" Jeff asked.

Ron guffawed so hard and loud that Jeff nixed the delivery of future one-liners.

So, to Customer, Jeff cannot point again at the coupon language, which, because it would be repetition, could be interpreted as condescension. He cannot say, "You are right, but . . ." because it is both a concession and a denial. He can only stick to the blank, the vacuous. "I'm very sorry."

Sometimes Customer will ask for a manager, which is a relief. Always, Customer, their brow knit in frustration, will take a moment to glare at Jeff with a look that indicates how beneath them he is.

There are now nine people in line. The mundanity of the job also lets Jeff see more easily when there is a line, which makes him feel like he needs to be faster. He goes plenty fast as it is, but he can see the people—each one of them—waiting. They look at him, and he knows some think he could be going faster, or the store (represented by him in that moment) is negligent in not assigning more cashiers. He can see that some will be grumpy by the time they reach him. They won't even look at him. That is, unless something goes wrong, in which case they won't take their eyes from him.

A figure fast-walks through the store's entrance, and Jeff looks to see Tracy. He turns to the register clock (she's thirty-four minutes late) and then back to her. When their eyes lock, instead of mouthing an apology, she looks down and grits her teeth. He's not even sure what sort of consolation this expression is supposed to be. Her shoes make a bristly scraping sound against the carpet as she moves past Cosmetics to the break room.

Tracy is a high school student, a part-timer. In a few weeks it will be summer, and her hours per week will jump from eighteen to thirty-two, and then, in August, she'll vanish into college. Jeff finds relief in the notion. He can't help but pay attention to what she's doing when she's nearby, and often what she's doing is wrong. Jeff can hear her engage with customers and see every bad move she makes as things escalate. Does she shout at them? Does she curse? No, but when a difficult situation could be defused through some show of comportment, she is more likely to stand back, cross her arms, and reflect back the same energy given to her. No good. The customer might ask for a manager, but because Jeff is there and five years older than Tracy, they will turn to him as if *he* is the manager. First, through mollification, he will need to undo the hostility she's brought about. Then he'll need to repeat the conversation they just had, substituting his own deference for Tracy's sass.

Tracy stocks shelves incorrectly (right product, wrong size, or right brand, wrong color). Alice or Ron will notice and point out to her that when in doubt she can be sure by double-checking the UPC code on the item against the shelf tag. She'll say, "Oh, thanks. Nobody told me that," which is annoying, because Jeff told her that. He trained five people before her, and he tells *all* of them that. It's like she's trying to incriminate him through the Transitive Property of Screwup.

When Tracy is on register, her cell phone is in her hand or beside the till. She plays games, or texts. Her vision angles down at the phone, so when Jeff and Tracy are both on register and a customer stands five feet back waiting for a signal, they never get it from her. (Jeff has played chicken a few times by keeping his eyes averted, but the act of noticing customers and pretending not to is too unnatural for him to maintain with any regularity.)

Tracy's boyfriend sometimes meets her for lunch breaks or smoke breaks. He wears loose-fitting tank tops (even in winter, under a worn-down coat), and a white-and-green ball cap, the brim flat and turned askew. The boyfriend (Alex? Andrew?) smiles and nods and touches Jeff's shoulder as if the two of them are great buddies, as if any minute Alex/Andrew will invite Jeff to get high with them, or go to McDonald's, or hang out with the other kids after hours in the Regent Center parking lot until asked to disperse by the police.

For a person who dresses and walks like he's some antiestablishment street kid who can't afford T-shirts with sleeves, Alex/Andrew is kind of good-looking. He has a practiced smile, teeth in a lovely, pearly row. His skin is so clear, it's like he bathed for weeks in high-end Aisle 9 products before stepping out, even though Jeff knows Alex/Andrew just turned seventeen, which means his face should be inflamed and erupting with acne. Jeff knows that one day Alex/Andrew will ditch the cap and puffy coat in favor of business casual, which he will look equally at home in as he maneuvers himself up through the ranks of middle management toward the American Dream.

Jeff has seen Tracy sell Alex/Andrew packs of Parliaments, even though everyone assessed to be younger than twenty-seven must be carded in order to buy cigarettes. Ron says that police will ask minors to come in on occasion and try to purchase, and if they are allowed to, the store is fined and the cashier is fired. Tracy always asks for Alex/Andrew's ID for the benefit of the security cameras. One time Jeff was stocking diapers in Aisle 3 when he heard Alex/Andrew behind him.

"What's up, brother? Can you sell me a pack of cigarettes?"

Jeff kept his focus on the shelves.

"Please, man. Could you do this for me?"

At the same time, the bell sounded from the counter, a checker asking for another cashier to open. Jeff left the diapers and signed back into his register. The line of five people went down quickly, and Alex/Andrew had the luck of filtering to Jeff when his turn came. Jeff asked for his ID (seventeen in two months) and rang up the Parliaments. Alex/Andrew smiled his charmed smile and left.

Why had Jeff done it? Why had he given in to someone he didn't even like? But . . . he *did* like him, without knowing why, and he *hated* that he liked him. The world provided for Alex/Andrew whatever he needed (good looks, pretty girlfriend, cigarettes). He seemed so happy, so friendly. He was friendlier with Jeff than Tracy had ever been. Jeff could easily imagine Alex/Andrew's incredulity over any disappointment. Someone ought to say no to him so that he'd have practice with it, but it was too much work to say no to people like him. They always fought back, and they were always right on some level. If Jeff had said no, he would have been acting out of spite. That was another thing about Alex/Andrew—his ability to make a "right" action feel like a small, petty one.

Tracy had been in the break room for six minutes now. How long does it take to lock away a purse and don a vest?

"These are five for four dollars," an unhappy-looking woman says, dropping a mess of king-size peanut M&M's on the counter. When Jeff scans them, they come up full price.

"Your circular has them at five for four dollars," she says.

Jeff picks up his copy of the circular. A man in line a few spaces back adjusts his posture.

"This says it's for the plain M&M's, not the peanut." Jeff shows her the ad.

"So what? What's the difference?"

Peanuts. "The sale doesn't apply to these. Would you still—?" Before he finishes, she's walked off. He picks up the discarded M&M's and drops them in the return basket behind him.

Out of the corner of his eye, he sees Beige Trench Coat enter and walk with determination down the greeting card aisle. *Fuck.* Jeff apologizes to the next person in line and dials the manager's office. Alice doesn't answer. *Fuck. Oh well. But fuck.* She must have gone to the stockroom or bathroom. He debates calling over the store's PA for manager assistance, but the whole store would hear, including Beige Trench Coat, which would defeat the purpose. Jeff starts ringing the next customer.

"How's your day going?" the next customer says with too much enthusiasm.

"Okay."

"Long shift?"

"Yeah."

"Almost there, right?"

Why is she making conversation? "Almost."

"Then what?"

Jeff takes her in—she's maybe forty-five, with wavy brown hair, wire-frame glasses, a brown mole on the underside of her right cheek. She has an easy smile, the sort of smile you imagine being on her all day. The register makes an unhappy noise. Invalid UPC. Jeff has scanned the shipping bar code instead of the store code. He flips over the box of hair dye. "Uh . . . nothing."

"Quiet night at home, then?"

She could be his mother—happy to see him, curious about his life, empathetic to the point of selflessness—but he'd like her to stop talking. He ignores her last question and finishes scanning.

"Forty-seven eighty-two," he says.

She reaches into her purse, still smiling, and runs a credit card through the reader to her side.

"That one's not working," Jeff says, extending his hand.

"Thank you."

He swipes the card through his register, and they stand there as it processes. She won't meet his eyes now, but she still smiles—at the counter, the cigarette racks, the batteries. He knows she was only trying to be nice. She seems nice—the sort of person he could tell things to, who'd forgive him, who wouldn't judge him. How can it be that he no longer has the patience for a person like this? He smiles at her as best he can for the rest of the transaction. The smile feels strange on his face, like it must not look right, but she returns it as she takes her bag. "Enjoy your night," she says, and he thanks her.

Beige Trench Coat stands sixth in line. The coat is no longer draped over his right shoulder. He's wearing it. Such a prick. Jeff tells himself that he doesn't care. It's not his money, not his store. But people shouldn't be allowed to get away with shit, and Jeff shouldn't have to give in to people getting away with shit just because he can't *prove* it, even though he is sure that shit is being gotten away with.

Why the fuck isn't Tracy out here yet? He doesn't know why she hasn't been fired. Perhaps it's because he picks up her slack. Perhaps it's because Ron and Alice aren't on the ground with her like he is, so they don't know how bad things are. He'll say something to her. She knows she's late, so he'll just be repeating what she knows, what Alice or Ron will say and have said before. But he wants to say *something* no matter how small it makes him, so as not to just absorb it. She'll toss out an "I'm sorry," which has basically become her catchphrase, but he wants to make her mean it.

"Returns," Beige Trench Coat says, placing on the counter a breast pump, Pedialyte, Desitin, and a receipt that has clearly been run over by car tires in the parking lot several times. This is a good score for Beige Trench Coat. Probably his biggest take yet. Jeff asks him questions, knowing the answers.

"Anything wrong with them?"

"No."

"Would you like an exchange, or store credit?"

"Cash."

"Can I see ID?"

"Not carrying right now."

Jeff circles the items on the receipt, writes "returned," and punches them into the register. He hands over almost ninety-four dollars. Ninety-four dollars! As if Beige Trench Coat could have possibly had a breast pump and jug of Pedialyte under his coat when he came in instead of reverse-shopping up and down the aisles until he finished the Easter egg hunt for the items on his found receipt. Beige Trench Coat exits the store a few moments before Alice emerges from the bathroom and returns to the manager's office. Of course. Jeff will tell her later so that she can check the security tape, but Beige Trench Coat is something of a savant with camera angles.

Jeff hadn't felt this unhappy when he came in today. The feeling will last through tomorrow morning, possibly later, and even if it lifts by his next shift, it will surely barrel back toward him for another go. He used to have more patience, but these days he's like a raw nerve. Even the neutral shit—someone dropping cash on the counter instead of handing it to him, someone saying "Hi, um" instead of just "Hi" when he answers the phone—sets him off. Things had been kind of fun when he started at CVS two years ago as an unemployment stop-loss. Remembering those times is like watching home movies of his parents as children—these things happened, but these things could not possibly have ever happened.

Jeff once scaled the box pile in the stockroom to get the last pack of Charmin. "Get down from there!" Alice said, laughing.

"I promise not to sue," he said.

"That's not stable. Get down."

"Why would you stack your boxes in an unstable formation?"

"I'm serious. Come down right now."

"I will. I just need the Charmin as a ballast for the descent."

Then there was the night of the snowstorm a few days before Valentine's, when it was just Jeff and Ron on closing. No one had come in for over an hour, and Ron suggested they organize the seasonal aisle, which was a mess. Ron caught Jeff staring at the shimmering cleavage and glossy pectorals on the romance novel display. "Want me to . . . uh . . . put one of those aside for you?" Ron asked.

Jeff didn't know what made him do it. He opened one of the books and started reading. *"She clutched his powerful shoulders through the soft linen. 'He'll be back at nine thirty,' she said, possessed. 'Always nine thirty. Please.' 'I can't,' Raul said."*

"Put that down," Ron said.

"'I hate him, but he's my brother.' 'He's a monster,' she said back to him, her lips so near his neck. She wanted to taste him."

"Put it down, Jeff."

"Don't we need to be familiar with our merch? What if someone comes in asking for the best one?"

Ron shoved a pack of chocolates on the rack and stepped to the display. Jeff wondered for a moment if he was about to get reprimanded, but Ron picked up a different book, flipped it open, and pointed at the text: *Ride me, you fucking stallion! Ride me all the way to town and back!*

"Holy shit!" Jeff said.

"Beat that."

"Beat it?"

"Find something more stupid than that, okay? More ridiculous than that and you can go home early." Jeff and Ron spent another twenty minutes reading to each other and laughing until their stomachs hurt. Although some passages came close, nothing was as ridiculous. Ron let him leave early anyway.

They're all gone, those feelings, and it takes too much energy to fake them. A job he'd imagined as an interim solution to keep him from moving back home has somehow ballooned into what it is now, which is his whole life. When he returns to his apartment, it is only a break. His dreams speak to him in the language and symbols of the store, the beeps of the register, the whir of its cooling fan, the blank looks and aggressions of strangers. He cannot remember the last time he felt playful. He cannot remember the last time he had a crush on someone.

"This didn't work," a man says. He's over six feet tall, bald, wearing a blue dress shirt, open at the collar, and a black sport coat.

This is a hair and beard trimmer, one of the pricier ones. Jeff opens the box to make sure all the parts are inside.

"Cash, please," the man says.

"It's missing the charger."

"Everything it came with is in there."

"It says it comes with a charger. I'm not seeing it."

"Too bad for you," the man says.

"I'll call my manager down."

"Good move."

Alice answers the phone. The man stares down on him as he speaks. "I have a gentleman here with a return, but there's a part missing."

"Nothing's missing!" the man says. "Everything it came with is there!"

"I'll be down in three minutes."

Jeff hangs up. "She'll be down in a few minutes."

"Jesus Christ."

For a moment, the man doesn't move. With his meaty hand resting on the counter, he looks around as if surveying the inadequacy of the store. There are four people behind him.

"Could I have you . . . ?" Jeff falters with his words.

"What?"

"Could I have you step to the side for a moment?"

The man makes an unhappy noise and takes two small steps.

The next few customers are taken in the shadow of the man's displeasure. Some give Jeff sympathetic looks. Others are keen on paying and leaving.

Alice, who seems very small in comparison to this man, steps around the photo development station. "Can I help you?" she asks.

Jeff rings up Gatorade, a Hershey's bar.

"This is everything it fucking came with. I paid eighty dollars for this."

"Can I see the receipt?"

The bar code on a bottle of wine gets an angry beep from the register. Jeff checks a driver's license for the birthday and hands it back.

"I gave it to that guy."

Alice steps up to the counter. When Jeff has finished with his customer, she asks for it.

"He never gave it to me."

Though he has said it quietly, the man hears him.

"Oh, are you fucking kidding me? I gave you the receipt and the box and asked for cash."

Jeff feels his lips shaking. When he speaks, it is almost breathless. "I don't believe you gave me the receipt."

"Are you sure?" Alice asks.

Jeff nods.

"Fuck," the man says, making a big show of checking his pockets. "Well, I had it. I don't know. You must have it."

"I can give you store credit."

"Lady, I'll die before I spend another eighty dollars in this piece-of-shit store. Are you the manager?"

"I'm the assistant manager."

"What's your name?"

"Alice."

"And what's your boss's name?" He crosses his arms.

"Ron."

"Ron what?"

"Ron Wilkes."

"Ron Wilkes. What time is Ron Wilkes in tomorrow?"

"Seven a.m."

"Would you ask Ron Wilkes to expect a call from me, sweetie?"

"I'll let him know."

She hands him his box, and he marches out.

"Alice . . ." Jeff says.

She has already turned to go back upstairs, and she wheels around, eyes wide with undischarged fury.

"It can wait," he says.

She almost runs up to the manager's office.

Tonight has been awful. Maybe the worst, but the worsts all bleed into one another. After five or six people, there's an entirely new group of customers in line, and none of them has any idea what just happened. They only want their stuff. Jeff rings. He bags. He wipes his brow on his forearm. When he notices his right hand has clenched, he relaxes it, but when he notices it again a few moments later, it has reclenched. He wants to quit. He wants to quit so bad, but he's afraid that working this job for so long has condemned him to other jobs like it. The break room door opens.

Tracy wears her vest open. It puffs out a bit as she walks, and her hair flutters around her face. She steps behind the counter. Alice probably won't say anything to her, not now. Aside from the missed pay, there will be no punishment. Jeff feels his own misery pushing at him, about to burst. Tracy's a selfish, immature, unreliable fuckup who doesn't take her job—his job— seriously, and her behavior is unacceptable. It's not right. Jeff hasn't even finished with a customer when he spits her name out.

She jumps at his voice and turns. He's never seen her without makeup, and he can tell from the redness of her eyes that she's been crying. *What happened?* He doesn't know her well enough to ask. Something about tragedy, about sadness, about *her* sadness—something drains from him. It's as if the rest of the store has gone quiet. If she were a friend, he would know how to behave, but Tracy is not his friend. There is no scenario in which they'd be more to each other than what they are. He'd never imagined it bothering him.

"Are you okay?" he asks.

She nods in a way that says *Thanks for asking* and nothing else before turning back to her work.

He needs to go on break, but the line seems smaller now, more manageable, and he can wait until it is gone. They ring together in silence. He feels Tracy in the space beside him, and the weight of his own curiosity. As he rings, he keeps his attention not on his own customers, but on hers, listening to what they say, how they say it. He doesn't know what he'll do if one goes off on her, but then he does. He'll step beside her, insinuate himself, and look the customer in the eye until they look away from her. "Can I help you?" he'll say.

About the Author

KEVIN SKIENA received his MFA in creative writing from the University of Washington in 2006. He is a winner of the A. E. Hotchner Playwriting Competition and the Eugene Van Buren Prize for Fiction. His writing has appeared in *Hayden's Ferry Review*, *City Arts*, and *Gay City Anthology*. He is a cofounder and instructor of the Seattle-based Smudgy Notebook writers' workshop. He blogs at stilllifewithissues.wordpress.com.

JE NE SAIS QUOI

ELIZABETH LANGEMAK

I first saw you in a class
on theory where daily

I used words I understood
only in part. I stuttered

into the room like a girl
climbing a dark staircase

calling, *Is anyone there?*
In theory someone is

there but I'd been in school
so long I might not have

cared. Everyone's knowledge
seemed part of my own,

a well I could drink from
if I became thirsty. In theory

I was thirsty but not always
in practice. Our teacher

gave me a list of others
who struggled so I could

ask them for help but
I thought this bad practice

so I started reading
through you, my eyes

on your fingers as they fanned
through the thin textbook

pages. I learned only what
I should not have and forgot

what I knew. When we
finally met we spoke about

theory and then in theory
for years, parsing each other's

constructions of what
we thought might be love

and you would sometimes
yell *Gah!* and *Fuck!* like you

did when our teacher lectured
on Marx. I knew these

were the sounds of your
sounding. With practice

we decided which questions
were answers. Like so

many others, *marriage*
was a word I understood

only in theory. I thought
it meant something that happened

once and kept going but by then
I had some theories, too,

so I asked you
to practice and the practice

itself is a pleasure paid
to the debt of the theory,

to what it feels like to learn
something from nothing,

to the well we both drink from
that does nothing for thirst.

About the Author

ELIZABETH LANGEMAK'S poems have appeared or are forthcoming in publications such as *Shenandoah, Colorado Review, Literary Imagination*, the *Beloit Poetry Journal*, and *Best New Poets: 50 Poems by Emerging Writers*. She lives in Philadelphia, where she is an assistant professor of English at La Salle University. Find her online at elizabethlangemak.wordpress.com.

Maryanna Hoggatt © 2014

THE LAST KING OF OPEN ROADS

BRENDA PEYNADO

In 1979, our father took us on a ski trip. It was the last in a series of my father's ideas over the years to put the family back together, to show my mother he wasn't wrong to bring us to this new country. The trips were disasters, all of them.

Earlier that year, my father took us to the zoo on the day kids get in free, but it was also the day Gentle the Gorilla ate his trainer's finger and escaped. We drove to the Everglades but couldn't afford the tour, and the rickety boat my father borrowed from a Mexican peddling oranges sank into the swamp. Luckily, it was shallow enough to wade back. He took us to Satellite Beach, but a red tide had swept thousands of dead fish onto shore, and all of us had to plug our noses from the rot.

I forgave my father these disasters. I was nine years old, reading history books and radio manuals with squiggles I could barely decipher, and I worshipped him. He was a truck driver, and when he drove the big rig to the house, he would let me climb up into the cab, honk the horn, and make the air brake squeal. He looked like a master navigator behind the wheel, like he could find his way anywhere.

My brother, Alberto, who was twelve, was starting to sense that our father was not all I made him out to be. When I played in the truck, he'd taken to rolling his eyes and hiding from the neighbors.

Our mother knew my father for who he was: the master of nothing and no one. When he sent for her in the Dominican Republic, my brother was two and my mother was pregnant with me. My father had left Jarabacoa three months before to secure a job and a place en La Florida, so his daughter could be born a verdadera American. He'd found full-time employment as a truck driver because of a Dominican he knew; an uncle of a brother of a friend was in charge of the shipments.

My mother spent those early months of pregnancy learning English from a USAID nurse whom my mother sewed clothes for. On the plane ride over, Mami chatted with the flight attendants in her new English. Her full belly stretched her starched white dress, and she squeezed my brother's hand in excitement. The USAID nurse was from Denver, and told her how everything was better there, cleaner. When my mother arrived in Florida, she was expecting something glamorous, mountains even grander than in Jarabacoa, with pines instead of plantains, cities in the cleft of valleys whose skyscrapers reached into the heavens. But the town my father drove her home to was ugly and dry: Kissimmee, Florida. It wasn't even near the ocean, and there were no mountains to speak of. My mother said when she first saw Kissimmee and our squat, flimsy house, it's like Dios sat on the earth, and this is the mark of his culo.

The yearly disastrous vacations usually came a few weeks after my mother threatened to go back to the island. We knew if she went home, she'd never come back. Even I sensed, every time my father left on his long hauls, that I was to babysit her and make sure she didn't leave us. When I couldn't find her in the house, I'd start to cry until she emerged from the yard or the garage, asking me what was the matter.

Her childhood friends she hadn't seen in ten years had become more and more unavailable, and when she did manage to speak to them, she found they had almost nothing to say. She was terrified no one remembered her back on the island. I caught her in one of my searches, telephone cord leading into her closet, my mother pressed up against the dress forms she used to sew clothes, trying to hide the fact that she was racking up phone bills.

So when my father proposed a New Year's vacation, he was, as always, trying to fix things with her.

The plan was simple enough. He would take her to see Colorado and the American mountains she had fantasized about. He had to haul snowblower parts manufactured in Florida to a Denver warehouse, and he could bring us with him in the cab of his truck. We'd leave the day after Christmas and make it to the mountains in time for New Year's Eve. He would teach us how to ski, and he'd prove to her once and for all why he'd brought her to this country. Although we could afford less here than on the island, and even though we'd left our family behind, he could share with her the view of America from the road that he had grown to love. And he could show her fresh white snow— something she'd never seen before.

What a ridiculous proposal, my mother said. It's too expensive. You think the solution to our problems is loading us all up in your asqueroso, smelly truck and throwing us down a mountain?

———

That night, after I heard their raised voices in the kitchen, my mother acquiesced. They came out to the living room and announced we were driving to Denver.

I'd rather go somewhere warm and read comic books, Alberto said before locking himself in his room.

Then Papi turned on the news, like he did every night, the leather of the secondhand chair crumbling around his outline. Washes of light flooded the living room from bright pictures of politicians arguing over President Carter's policies. My father watched the news with such gravity, you would have thought he understood the English, understood what was happening to the country he had chosen. I had checked out all the American history books from the school library, determined to understand it for him, thinking that if only we could see the road clear before us, my father the navigator could steer us. If we could just find the way forward, my mother would stay, my father would be redeemed, and the country we lived in could finally be ours.

I translated the night's top headline for my father: Students in Tehran climb like ants over the walls of the US embassy and take hostages.

I had translated other events for him over the course of the year: The Soviet Union invades Afghanistan. The great Hurricane David kills over twelve hundred in the US and the Dominican Republic. One of the Unabomber's wooden contraptions failed to go off in the belly of a plane headed for Washington, DC. Saddam Hussein is inaugurated president of Iraq.

Maybe it was the state of the world, but my father looked miserable. Flashes of light from the TV colored his frown gray, and I took on the role I'd always taken, which was also my father's, trying to put things back together like a giant jigsaw puzzle. It was what I tried to do even after I married one of those "real" Americans whose Irish family had been here for generations and my parents were both in the ground.

Papi, I said, I can't wait until I see snow!

He turned from the TV and measured me with his eyes. He said, You need to promise me something. Keep your eye on your brother. You know how he is, always making trouble. We need to make sure everything goes smoothly this time.

It was true about my brother. At Satellite Beach, my brother threw dead fish at me, a smell I could not get out of my hair for weeks. At the zoo, he taunted the animals behind the cages.

I crossed myself. I promise I'll help, I said.

I don't know why you even bother, Mami said as she walked in. Just watch the Spanish channel. Turn that ple-pla off.

———

On Christmas Day, I woke up first and pulled Alberto out of his room. There were smaller boxes with each of our names on them, but there were huge boxes too, wrapped in brown packing paper. We were save-the-best-for-last kind of children, so we opened the small ones first. They were the troll doll and the Secret Identity Mego that we'd wanted, but much smaller versions than we'd asked for. My troll was three inches tall with his lime-green hair sticking straight up and the signature naked, fat belly. Alberto's was a knockoff Mego, smaller and uglier, with "Made in Hong Kong" stamped on the back of the packaging card. It wasn't even Clark Kent exactly. His glasses were wrong.

Mami and Papi came in once we finished inspecting the toys. We chimed our quiet gracias, and they opened their presents next. Mami gave Papi fuzzy slippers for driving in the cold. He said he loved them, picked her up, and gave her a kiss to say thank you.

Papi got Mami an eight-track: Pablo Neruda's *The Captain's Verses*.

Oh, she said softly, how wonderful.

I didn't understand the gift. We didn't have an eight-track player in the house, and I knew from a conversation I once overheard that *The Captain's Verses* was the only Neruda book she didn't like. Although I didn't know why at that point.

The only one that wasn't on your shelf, Papi said. And we can listen to it on the way to Colorado.

Oh, she said again, how wonderful.

Inside the big brown boxes were ski jackets, mittens, hats—cold-weather hand-me-downs from some related Dominicanos in Boston. The vacation was our present. Mami packed our bags. I found the Neruda eight-track hidden behind the bookshelf; she had intended on leaving it. I stole my father's keys and set the Neruda on his truck seat. Two days after Christmas, in the dark morning, we climbed the ladder steps and entered the purple cab of Papi's eighteen-wheeler.

———

I felt like we were aboard a spaceship, except filled with faux leather and wood panels. There was even a bed behind the front seats, where my father slept on long hauls. The dashboard array of lights glowed like planets, and the needles on the dials swiveled like broken compasses. The brakes groaned and hissed, and the CB radio, which my father couldn't understand, droned steadily. Papi had hung up pine-tree air fresheners like ornaments to cover the stench of cigar smoke that he kept puffing out the window. Alberto and I rolled around on the small bunk behind our parents. *The Captain's Verses* intoned on repeat.

Once we crossed out of Florida, the air got cold even with the heat blowing, so we suited up in our ill-fitting jackets. I could tell my brother was proud that his was his favorite color, neon orange. He kept rubbing the worn sleeves. I'd brought my troll with me, and I clung to it, played with it, and imagined it could tell me the future if I rubbed its hideous belly.

But it didn't tell me that thirty years later I would be driving this same interstate, leaving my own husband behind, with my children not yet understanding what was happening. And if they'd known, would they have treasured their last moments with their father together as a family? Or like me, would they have looked out the window, the country flying by them like a map with borders so invisible that they wouldn't know they had crossed over until the betrayal was done.

Mami had brought dominoes for us, but the ivory rectangles wouldn't stay in lines on the bed and ended up scattered all over the cab like an infestation, along with Alberto's M&M's. Mami would sometimes squeeze my hand from the front seat, but for the most part, she just looked out the passenger window for the three-day ride. Alabama, Louisiana, and Texas passed before our eyes with little acknowledgment from her, except for occasional deeps sighs of stale regret. On the fifth time *The Captain's Verses* started over, a deep voice intoning *Today, it was all the earth, in a lightning flash, dawn. In that territory, walking, walking, walking, I shall spend my life.* Mami asked Papi to turn it off. He thought she was insisting out of politeness and left it on.

Alberto was finally excited. He whispered to me, Maybe out here Papi's a superhero, the last of his alien kind. The King of Open Roads. He saves hitch-hikers and stray dogs. Maybe they yell, King! on the CB, and that's the signal for him to save someone. Maybe we're his supersecret identity, this terrible cover. I never want to go back to Kissimmee.

Kiss-ih-me, I said, and I puckered my lips, and my brother squirmed and shrieked until my father bellowed, Ténse quietos! And we were.

———

When we reached Denver, we could see the Rockies, jagged and marbled with white. Mami said the white starkness was terrible, that everything was dead except the evergreens. But I caught her smiling as she looked out the window to the mountains. Alberto grabbed the CB radio and whooped into it, yelling King! and warning all the truckers of grizzlies. I just stared; the white landscape was like nothing I'd seen. Papi raised his eyebrows at my mother. Look at the glorious gift I've given you, all these grand mountains carved by glaciers, he seemed to say.

By the time we reached the ski trails, it was already late into the afternoon. Mami jammed hats on each of our heads and deposited us on the icy pavement. Papi blared the truck's horn, as if people hadn't already noticed we'd arrived.

The truck took up five parking spaces. People in soft scarves and Vuarnet sunglasses stared as we unloaded the giant purple cab. Other families had their skis mounted to the roofs of their cars. Papi couldn't conceal his excitement as he stretched and put on his ski pants over his jeans, making a big show of it. I tried to put the hood up on my jacket, but the string had long since broken, and the hood kept falling down, exposing my embarrassment.

A little boy asked his father if *that family* was actually going to ski. My mother understood him and clenched her jaw. My father gave an Epa! as we headed toward the ski shop. I stuck my tongue out at the boy. My brother waved, his jacket too short and coming up almost to his elbow as he lifted his arm.

———

Inside the ski shop, a man who reeked like skunk and gasoline ratcheted my feet into boots, which smelled like the worst sicote and mashed my feet stiff. The man ignored my complaints and tried to speak to my father instead.

No Inglish, Papi said.

The ski-shop man shrugged and told him, It's really cold today, frostbite cold. You need to cover up. He mimicked someone shivering with their arms crossed. He asked if my father wanted a harness to put on me so that I couldn't get too far away or out of control. He held the leash out and dangled it, as if I were a dog. Rental, he made sure to say. Only two dollars.

I refused to translate, but my brother was more than willing to sacrifice me to the horrible leash. I tried to kick him with the boots, but as soon as I lifted one, I fell over.

Papi nodded at the harness. Good idea, he said. The man asked the same about my brother, and with a smirk on my face, I translated. But my father clapped my brother on the back and shook his head. Mi hijo, he said, he will do fine on his own.

When it was Mami's turn to get measured for boots, she shook her head. You go on without me, she said.

Ay, no, my father said. Hold everything. We're all going together, no?

No way am I getting on those two little palitos and sliding down like a loca, she said.

But what about the vacation? he pleaded.

You show the kids a good time. I'll be breathing in the mountain air and enjoying not breaking my leg. She handed him a hat she'd made for him, his old nickname sewn across the front—Neil—for his obsession with Neil Armstrong and the space race when he was in school.

Mami, wait, I said.

People gawked as we yakked in our loud foreign voices.

Shoulders back, mustering all the grace she had, my mother walked toward the lodge, telling us that we'd meet in the cafeteria later.

———

To put the skis on, you had to stomp into them with a vengeance, which I thought was fun. There was great commotion everywhere as we waited to go up the mountain—stomping boots, ratcheting buckles, creaking snow, and the mechanical drone of the lift. My father put on his hat so that it only covered the tip-top of his head, and he hummed, moving his hips while we waited in line.

Then, the chair scooped us up, and the ruckus of the lift line fell away. Papi told us to hang on for dear life. If anything dropped, it would be lost forever in the snow. The cold found every hole in our layers and slid in, finding its way to the tops of my ears, the back of my neck, and my wrists, where the jacket was too short to cover them. From way up, the white ground was peppered by neon jackets and packs of skiers in formations. From way up, they looked like balls rolling down against their will, pawns of gravity.

Some of those people are going really slow, Alberto said. They look like little abuelos taking a walk. If I get really good, I'm going to ski down through the trees. That silly wide trail is for viejos. For the elderly.

You can't. It's too dangerous. I'm going to hide your Mego if you do, I said.

Yup, he said. Just watch. I'll be better than you. You're going to be terrible with that stupid harness.

Papi, I said. He's bothering me.

My brother pushed me into the metal bar holding us all in, and the chair swayed like it was dancing. I screamed. I didn't want to get lost in the snow forever. Papi grabbed the back of my jacket.

Stop, he growled at my brother.

To me he said, You don't think I'd let anything happen to you, do you?

I looked at my father and his faded ski outfit and his Neil hat, and I thought, as long as I stayed close to him, I'd be OK.

It turns out we would inherit our parents' flaws. Alberto was like my father, a dreamer with a penchant for trouble, fighting every battle that came his way. Against all my wishes, I inherited my mother's perpetual unhappiness. At least I did eventually leave Kissimmee with my children.

That ski trip was the last vacation my father would take me on, but I didn't know it yet. I let the chair sway us like it was rocking us to sleep, wind whistling past.

———

My brother rocketed down the slopes. My father shouted, 'Pera! My brother responded, Hurry up! and continued out of control on the two narrow planks he was standing on. Papi held on to my leash and kept it taut, so all I had to do was sit back on my haunches, and the tight boots and my father kept me up. We slid into trails the signs called "Snowflake" and "Easy Rider" and "Klondike." My breath dimmed my mask with fog. Years afterward I realized love could blind you like that—love for your father, or love for one country or another. You could ski off a cliff, blind like that, and for a moment feel like you're flying.

During one run, Alberto whooped in front of us. Then I hit a bump and was flung up like a jack-in-the-box. Coño! my father yelled. I could feel him struggling with the harness and trying to steer us to safety. I was jerked into hops like a puppet on a string.

Moguls! my brother shouted, and then out of a tiny clear spot in my goggles, I saw his skis go flying and heard a crash.

Alberto! my father yelled, still up the mountain.

My brother struggled to his feet. I'm OK! he yelled back. He set his skis right and kicked himself back into them.

We are never taking Bonanza again, my father said.

Woo! my brother shouted. That was rad!

Then we were back up the lift, Papi pointing the way down again with his gloved finger. Skiers peeled by us in sudden whooshes. The landscape blurred by me in snippets of snow and trees, the tips of the mountains pushing their points into the inflated balloon of the sky, almost bursting.

———

After hours of this, we met my mother at the bottom to eat. We sat at a table in the crowded cafeteria filled with the sour smell of sweaty fleece jackets. I was starving, and my toes were numb.

So how did it go? Mami asked us as we ate, but she was looking at Papi, preparing to defend us against another of his disasters.

My brother said it was awesome. Chulo.

OK, I said, but then I changed my mind. Actually, it really was chulo, I said.

Really? That's great, she said, her eyebrows arching. Well, at least the mountains live up to expectations.

I hugged my father, and again Mami said, Que bueno. And you could tell she meant it, too. She was glowing, although maybe it was the cold. It felt like the tide of her unhappiness and dissatisfaction was beginning to turn. I saw that my mother was willing to give things a chance, if only something would go right.

For all the fear my mother injected into us, she was the one who made us dinner every night, sewed new clothes for us so that we wouldn't look ragged at school, and worried about practical things. When I turned eighteen and vouched for her to get her citizenship, I would see this tired hope in her again, hand raised up beside her, pledging allegiance to the flag, while a president she'd never meet congratulated her from a prerecorded tape.

Maybe it would have been fun, Mami said.

My brother shed his suspenders and then his gloves.

Don't get too comfortable, Papi said. We're going back up.

But I can't feel my hands, Alberto said. I can't ski when I can't feel my fingers or toes. Cold weather is, like, my Kryptonite.

Real superheroes keep fighting, my father said. It's New Year's Eve. They're turning the lights on and letting people ski at night, and our tickets last until ten. We don't want to waste them.

Are you sure that's a good idea? my mother said.

Mami should come! I said.

Yes, why not? my father said. Make the most of it?

Bueno, she said hesitantly and smiled.

———

As we went up the mountain again, I dozed off between my parents to the slow rocking of the chairlift, and the wind whistling in my ears. Even my brother was tired, but I heard Papi tell him, Don't we want to show Mami a good time?

Alberto elbowed me. My father was telling us that he started hauling big rigs because he'd wanted to travel. Then he pointed to his Neil hat and told me he was pretty sure I was conceived on the night Armstrong walked on the moon.

Why would you tell her that? my mother said.

Don't you remember my tíos came over to watch on your mother's TV set? And then all your cousins brought over a sancocho and dragged us out to dance? I bet tonight will be like that, with the New Year, my father said.

We'll see, Mami said.

At that point, the peaks were steeped in orange. Then the sky turned blue-gray, and lights turned on, spreading like a wave up the trails. Below our dangling feet, glimmering paths veined the mountains, every one of them urgent and calling us down.

We took a few easy runs, and it looked like my mother had gotten the hang of going incredibly slow without falling too often. Papi was showing her how to make wedges with her skis. When she fell, she laughed and leaned against him. Alberto had graduated from wedges; he kept pointing his skis straight down the mountain to pick up speed.

Let's do Smiling Elf, my father said when we'd reached the bottom again.

Papi, Alberto said, Smiling Elf is too boring.

Boring is good, Mami said, still struggling to stay balanced on her skis.

We have to get down somehow, Papi said.

I'm not going down unless it's fun, Alberto said.

And what would be fun? my mother asked.

Bonanza, my brother said, grinning. The one with all the bumps.

Ni lo pienses, my father said. No way.

Bumps do not sound like fun, my mother said to my father. You took them on bumps? I told you to be careful.

Why do you have to go as slow as a vieja? Alberto said. It's no fun with you here, Mami.

Alberto, my father warned. He looked at his watch and said, We just have an hour more until ten. This will be our last time up.

My brother was ready to mutiny. My hands are cold, he said, and you guys take too long.

One more time, Papi said. We have to get down somehow. I'll buy you M&M's at the top.

Stop being a brat, I said.

Alberto looked a little ashamed of himself, but not ashamed enough. I thought maybe if he wasn't around, Mami and Papi could actually enjoy themselves. I decided I would live up to my promise to my father to make sure everything went right.

We were dragged into the boisterous lift line again. I inched along between Alberto and my parents. I said to Alberto what I thought I needed to say for the sake of all of us, knowing what he would do next. I knew exactly the right button to push, as siblings do, to send my brother careening down his own road.

But what did I know then about roads? I thought the future could be controlled with enough studying, like news anchors making sense of the week's events. But roads—yellow brick roads, pavement roads, pebbled paths—were nothing but figments of our imagination.

The hollering of the drunks was just loud enough that no one but Alberto could hear me. You're too good for this trail now, I whispered to him. Look at that silly wide path with all those viejos.

———

At the top, we found out that the lodge was closed.

You shouldn't have bribed him, Mami said. She reminded Alberto that there were M&M's in the truck, if we just went down this one more time.

Now look who's bribing him, Papi said.

Alberto took off ahead of us, toward Bonanza.

Stop! my father yelled as my brother darted over a ledge and out of our sight.

Skiers zipped by us carving powerful turns, back and forth around the moguls, spraying snow into the glowing lamplight.

When we reached the top of Bonanza, Alberto was nowhere to be found. Skiers continued to pass us left and right.

Alberto, my mother called. Alberto!

Don't worry about him, I insisted. He'll be fine.

But after a couple of minutes, I became worried. I knew he wasn't good enough to make it all the way down through the trees.

Let me tell you, my mother said to my father, he takes after you.

I don't know what you mean by that.

If you don't know, then I'm not going to tell you.

Stop! I said. It's my fault. I told him to go off the trail.

You're just a child, she said.

Those words stung hard and deep. I flung my hat into the snow, then picked it up. I am not a child, I said.

My mother ignored me. I'll go to the bottom in case he's waiting for us.

She flew straight down, without bothering to make a wedge.

My father continued to call out and ski, dragging me with him. I felt helpless and guilty, like he must have felt most days since bringing the family to America. I started to cry and then swallowed it, determined, like my father, to revise my mistake.

Halfway down, he decided we must have passed Alberto, and my father took off our skis so that we could climb back up. After only five steps of following uphill in those heavy boots, my legs burned, my head pounded, and I felt woozy. I couldn't find enough air to fill my lungs.

Papi, I said, I can't do it.

Do you want me to leave you here?

I shook my head. It was cold and dark.

I managed another ten steps up the mountain before my father turned around, concerned he might lose me as well.

¡Ayuda! ¡Auxilio! He waved his arms so that the skiers swishing by us would help, but nobody stopped. He kept calling out, but nobody understood him.

I asked people in English if they had seen a twelve-year-old boy, but nobody had.

We stood at the edge of the trail and yelled into the darkness. Nothing answered us back. My father was helpless.

I want to go down, I said.

When a ski patroller on a snowmobile appeared at the top of the slope, Papi flagged him down and started spouting in Spanish: ¡Mi hijo está perdido en los árboles! Él no es buen esquiador. Por favor, necesitas ayudarnos!

The patroller looked at him—his hand-me-down clothes and his Hispanic features—curled his lip in disgust, and turned away. I wished my father could keep it together—like the King of Open Roads, like he did behind the wheel of his truck—but all he could do was ball up his fists like he was going to fight the man.

I yanked on the ski patroller's jacket. Mister, I said, my brother is missing.

I was mashed between my father and the patroller on the snowmobile. The patroller radioed to the base, but there was no one down there fitting Alberto's description. We rode back up to the scene of his disappearance, the mogul field on Bonanza. The snowmobile roared through the dark, then stopped, illuminating a thin path of light off the trail and into the trees. We saw a deer and a small animal's eyes. The cold wind whipped into my face, my nose kept running, and I started crying again.

Above us, a sudden whistle and then a boom, like a plane dive-bombing and crashing. Fireworks, I shouted. The first boom was followed by five short bursts, which expanded into giant purple and red dandelions. The sound echoed off the mountains like the rushing of giant turbines. The light spread over the landscape, plain as day for a second here, a second there. Then a flash of neon orange popped out between the trees.

My father and the patroller jumped off the snowmobile and raced into the woods. They lifted my brother out of the snowdrift he was half buried in. He told me later he had almost given up trying to dig himself out.

I thought Alberto would be fine after he'd been found. But my brother was already on his own path. He would go on to serve three tours in Afghanistan and then Iraq. After his tours, when I'd already left the American, I drove him home to stay with us. My three boys adored their uncle Berto with his crazy ideas and his strange ranting when nothing went right. They crawled all over him, and when Alberto would wake up screaming with terror in the night in Spanish that there were bombs under the road or that he couldn't see the shooter through the smoke, my children, who didn't understand Spanish, would laugh as they set up sleeping bags to spend the night in his room—as if they already knew they would have to protect him. They were already from a different world.

Back in Colorado, my father kept clapping Alberto on the back. I contented myself to watch the rest of the fireworks show. The world erupted into tarantulas, chandeliers, maps, strings in a knot, like my family, and it all exploded.

———

The patroller set Alberto on the snowmobile between me and my father, and I could feel his arms holding on to me. He whispered to me that he'd thought he was going to die in that drift. Happy New Year, I whispered back.

We roared off to base on our skinny little ray of headlight as the fireworks finale bombed the sky. Concussions pounded our chests. The last firework glittered toward us like a galaxy of dying jets. Then, silence and ghost trails of smoke disintegrated over us. And just like that, it was the year 1980.

The year Walter Cronkite announced his retirement from the *CBS Evening News*. Mount St. Helens erupted, gray plumes of ash rising over the Northwest, helicopters and reporters struggling to capture it on film. The Unabomber struck again. Iraq invaded Iran. Crowds held vigil outside the apartment building where John Lennon was killed, and we listened to his voice over a speaker system from just the day before when he was still alive, saying, *We survived the upheaval of the world and we're going into an unknown future.*

Just like that, it was 1980, the year my father passed.

When we got to the base, people were blowing party whistles and shouting Happy New Year! Mami was frantic, screaming at my father until she saw Alberto, blue with cold.

The patroller pushed aside all the happy drunks and set Alberto next to the fire in the lodge. He took off my brother's jacket, hat, and gloves. Alberto's fingers were gray and stiff. The ski patroller dipped Alberto's hands in a bowl of lukewarm water. When his fingers slid in, my brother flinched.

That's good, the patroller said. If you can feel it, it means you won't lose your fingers.

My mother held Alberto and me each under an arm. I'll never forget the way she looked at my father then, her face full as I'd ever seen it with disgust. You're supposed to keep my children safe, she said. Que pendejo.

My father never got the chance to redeem himself. In those last three months after the ski trip, my mother wouldn't speak to him anymore, except to say she was going to leave him and to tell him things like, It's not you, it's this country that will never let me be happy; it's not you, it's how alone I feel here when things go wrong; it's not you, it's all of us. She started making sense for the first time in my life.

Then that March, when my father was hauling gasoline for Shell, his truck fell off a bridge on an interstate over a Louisiana swamp, and the rig exploded. The trucking company said he fell asleep at the wheel from his own negligence and wouldn't pay the insurance amount. My mother was stranded in this country with us. To this day, she says the company schemed us out of our rightful due, of the thing that would have turned our lives around.

My father stayed up some nights, sleepless in front of the TV, for hours trying to discern words out of the fog of English. Out of guilt, I would stumble into the living room in my pajamas, and he would let me translate. The hostages in Iran stayed captive. Reagan amassed vote after vote in the primaries. Walter Cronkite signed off with *And that's the way it is.* Papi watched and I watched the way it was, trying to decipher the code—why our lives were like this, what we were becoming, how to understand America—as if that could piece our family back together.

———

The morning after my brother got lost, my mother tossed me out of the motel bed while it was still dark. The furnace rasped out heat, and she crammed all of our things back into their bags. Alberto couldn't hold anything with his frostbitten hands, so my mother dressed him. My father solved his grief by ordering everyone from one side to the other in the tiny room, then prodding us into the truck cab.

As he started the engine, my father switched the CB on and then off, and started the Neruda eight-track at the beginning again. My mother didn't even notice. When I started to hear *The verses of the captain . . . the furies . . . in you the earth* for the twelfth time that trip, I could feel a little ball of sorrow in my throat, choking me.

When my father turned off the engine and got out of the cab to get gas, the silence was a relief. Across the street, the relics of Christmas lights were still up and blinking. An American flag waved in a shop window, like a wizard's curtain with no one behind it.

My father, the Last King of Open Roads, slammed the heavy door shut, started the ignition, and swung back onto the interstate. Dominoes skittered underneath my swinging feet. I realized I'd left the troll next to the motel bed, but I said nothing. Snow blew up off the road from the tires of cars. Doomed snowflakes hurtled toward the windshield like missiles. A blizzard was forming, but we didn't realize it yet.

Papi told my mother he'd forgotten the snow chains, and he gripped the steering wheel hard. Mami hummed herself a song in Spanish to keep calm, some melody I didn't recognize, as Neruda crooned, *Tied, we went down to sink without untwining . . . the rose of my echoing country . . . Perhaps your dream drifted from mine . . . my eyes and close them.* Beside me, my brother waved his frostbitten hands in front of my face and whispered Kiss-ih-me over and over to make me cry.

And just like that, the blizzard came. The road I thought my father had carved out for us disappeared before our eyes. Keep your eyes on the road, Papi said, and we stared into the furious white.

About the Author

BRENDA PEYNADO is a writer of stories, nonfiction, and other exaggerations. Her work appears or is forthcoming in the *Threepenny Review*, *Black Warrior Review*, *Cimarron Review*, *Pleiades*, and others. She received her MFA from Florida State University, where she was a Kingsbury Fellow, and her BA from Wellesley College. She is currently on a Fulbright grant to the Dominican Republic, writing a novel about the 1965 civil war and American intervention.

MEET THE ILLUSTRATORS

After a nomadic childhood spent doodling, eating, sleeping, and growing, **MICHAEL HIRSHON** ended up in Saint Louis, where he studied illustration and design. He's currently in New York City, in the Illustration as Visual Essay master's program at the School of Visual Arts. His clients include the *New York Times*, American Express, the *Washington Post*, and AARP. His work has been recognized by the Society of Illustrators, *3x3*, *American Illustration*, *Creative Quarterly*, *CMYK*, and the AIGA. To learn more about Michael, visit www.hirshon.net.

FORSYTH HARMON is an artist and writer based in New York. She received a BA in visual arts and an MFA from Columbia University. Her work has most recently appeared in the *Asian American Literary Review*, on the cover of Marisa Crawford's *8th Grade Hippie Chic*, and in a group benefit show at Bridgette Mayer Gallery. She is finishing an illustrated novel called *The Woo*, is inspired by everything from William Blake to *The Baby-Sitters Club*, and spends lots of time listening to certain songs on repeat. You can find her work at forsythharmon.com.

KEITH CARTER was born in 1978 in Tacoma, Washington, and went to Western Washington University in Bellingham, where he received his BA in fine arts. He later went to Pacific Northwest College of Art, but left a year before completion of his BFA to accept a job at Seattle design firm Ames Bros, where he worked for two years. He currently lives in Portland, Oregon, and spends most of his time painting pictures of animals and people. See more of his work at kcarterart.com.

BROOKE WEEBER, based in Portland, Oregon, finds her inspiration from various natural landscapes, as well as Greek and Native American culture. She has been drawing since she was a young thing but started focusing on it in high school and college. After receiving her BFA in painting from the University of Oregon in 2003, Brooke fled her native Northwest for the big city, where she focused on her other passion—professional baking. She received a degree in professional pastry baking from the French Culinary Institute of New York in 2005 and worked as a high-end cake decorator. Craving more trees and more drawing space, Brooke packed up her apartment and rerooted herself in Portland in 2009. She has been cranking out art pieces ever since and has had shows at Mississippi Studios, The Farm Café, and Tribute Gallery.

MARYANNA HOGGATT was born in the Philippines and raised in the dusty deserts of Arizona. She now resides in the rainy forests of the Pacific Northwest with her partner, Jake, and feline son, Theo. She spends most of her days painting and drawing Battle Animals in her home studio in Portland, Oregon.

ACKNOWLEDGMENTS

Thank you to our wonderful contributors.

Special thanks to Courtney Dodson, *Day One*'s fantastic poetry editor.

Thank you to the team at Amazon Publishing: Ed Park, Serra Hagedorn, Ashley Saleeba, Chrissy Wiley, Kris Beecroft, Daphne Durham, Jeff Belle, Amy Hosford, Tara Parsons, Brent Fattore, Justin Renard, Alexandra Woodworth, Maggie Sivon, Erin Pursell, Gabriella Page-Fort, Lan Trinh, Sarah Funk, Jimmy Healey, Elaine Bongiorno, Michael Temple, Megan Jacobsen and Vivian Lee.

DAY ONE

COVER GALLERY

DAY ONE
ISSUE 1

Fiction by **Rebecca Adams Wright**
Poetry by **Zack Strait**
Cover Art by **Forsyth Harmon**

DAY ONE
ISSUE 2

Fiction by **Clare Beams**
Poetry by **Morgan Parker**
Cover Art by **Keith Carter**

DAY ONE
ISSUE 3

Fiction by **Michael X. Wang**
Poetry by **Matthew Zingg**
Cover Art by **Maryanna Hoggatt**

DAY ONE
ISSUE 4

Fiction by **Heather Monley**
Poetry by **Jameson Fitzpatrick**
Cover Art by **Keith Carter**

DAY ONE
ISSUE 5

Fiction by **Bridget Clerkin**
Poetry by **Sarah Blake**
Cover Art by **Michael Hirshon**

DAY ONE
ISSUE 6

Fiction by **Antonio Ruiz-Camacho**
Poetry by **Elizabeth Gollan**
Cover Art by **Forsyth Harmon**

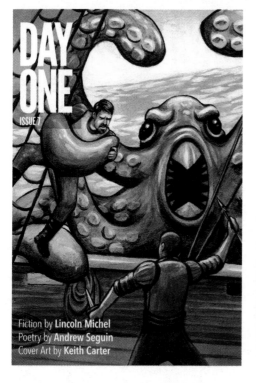

DAY ONE
ISSUE 7

Fiction by **Lincoln Michel**
Poetry by **Andrew Seguin**
Cover Art by **Keith Carter**

DAY ONE
ISSUE 8

Fiction by **Bae Suah,** Translated by **Sora Kim-Russell**
Poetry by **Mary-Kim Arnold**
Cover Art by **Michael Hirshon**

ISSUE 9

Fiction by **Jenny Halper**
Poetry by **Paul Hlava**
Cover Art by **Maryanna Hoggatt**

ISSUE 10

Fiction by **Sara Schaff**
Poetry by **Alissa Quart**
Cover Art by **Forsyth Harmon**

ISSUE 11

Fiction by **Theo Schell-Lambert**
Poetry by **Daniel Carter**
Cover Art by **Brooke Weeber**

ISSUE 12

Fiction by **Caroline Zancan**
Poetry by **Sam Donsky**
Cover Art by **Keith Carter**

DAY
ONE
ISSUE 13

Fiction by **Keziah Weir**
Poetry by **Christopher Phelps**
Cover Art by **Michael Hirshon**

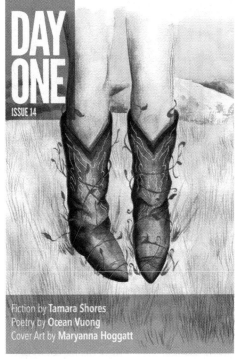

DAY
ONE
ISSUE 14

Fiction by **Tamara Shores**
Poetry by **Ocean Vuong**
Cover Art by **Maryanna Hoggatt**

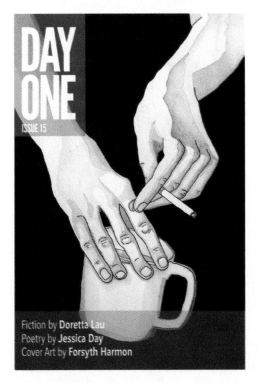

DAY
ONE
ISSUE 15

Fiction by **Doretta Lau**
Poetry by **Jessica Day**
Cover Art by **Forsyth Harmon**

DAY
ONE
ISSUE 16

Fiction by **Kilby Allen**
Poetry by **Nate Marshall**
Cover Art by **Brooke Weeber**

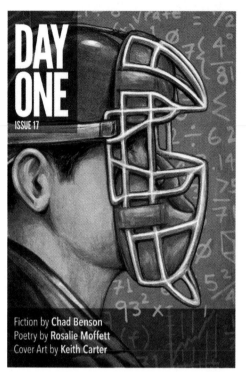

DAY ONE

ISSUE 17

Fiction by **Chad Benson**
Poetry by **Rosalie Moffett**
Cover Art by **Keith Carter**

DAY ONE

ISSUE 18

Fiction by **Jessica Pishko**
Poetry by **Jared Harel**
Cover Art by **Michael Hirshon**

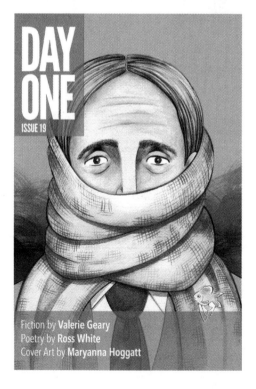

DAY ONE

ISSUE 19

Fiction by **Valerie Geary**
Poetry by **Ross White**
Cover Art by **Maryanna Hoggatt**

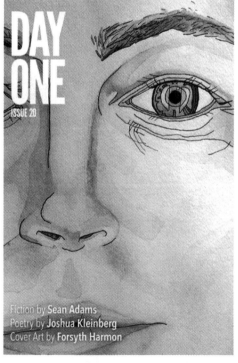

DAY ONE

ISSUE 20

Fiction by **Sean Adams**
Poetry by **Joshua Kleinberg**
Cover Art by **Forsyth Harmon**

Fiction by **Anna Swartz**
Poetry by **Montreux Rotholtz**
Cover Art by **Brooke Weeber**

Fiction by **Chris Feliciano Arnold**
Poetry by **Jeff Baker**
Cover Art by **Keith Carter**

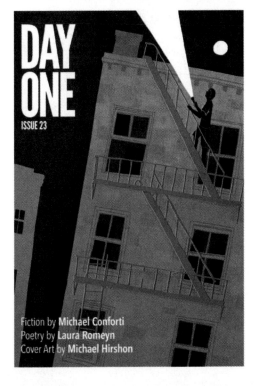

Fiction by **Michael Conforti**
Poetry by **Laura Romeyn**
Cover Art by **Michael Hirshon**

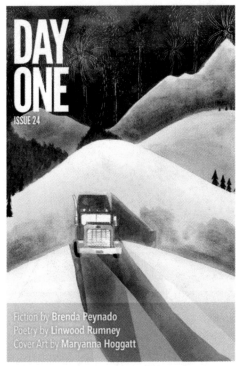

Fiction by **Brenda Peynado**
Poetry by **Linwood Rumney**
Cover Art by **Maryanna Hoggatt**

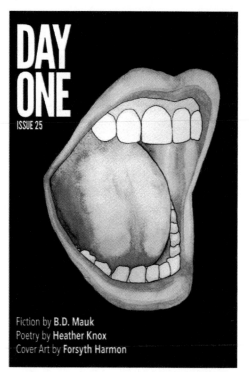

DAY ONE

ISSUE 25

Fiction by **B.D. Mauk**
Poetry by **Heather Knox**
Cover Art by **Forsyth Harmon**

DAY ONE

ISSUE 26

Fiction by **Ann Rushton**
Poetry by **Julia Anna Morrison**
Cover Art by **Brooke Weeber**

DAY ONE

ISSUE 27

Fiction by **LaTanya McQueen**
Poetry by **L.J. Sysko**
Cover Art by **Keith Carter**

DAY ONE

ISSUE 28

Fiction by **Tércia Montenegro**
Poetry by **Elizabeth Langemak**
Cover Art by **Michael Hirshon**

DAY
ONE
ISSUE 29

Fiction by **Nicole Haroutunian**
Poetry by **Micah Bateman**
Cover Art by **Maryanna Hoggatt**

DAY
ONE
ISSUE 30

Fiction by **Helen Rubinstein**
Poetry by **Justin Runge**
Cover Art by **Forsyth Harmon**

DAY
ONE
ISSUE 31

Fiction by **Elias Lindert**
Poetry by **Danielle Mitchell**
Cover Art by **Maryanna Hoggatt**

DAY
ONE
ISSUE 32

Fiction by **Michael B. Yang**
Poetry by **Melissa Barrett**
Cover Art by **Keith Carter**

DAY ONE

ISSUE 33

Fiction by **Peter Kispert**
Poetry by **Adrienne Raphel**
Cover Art by **Michael Hirshon**

DAY ONE

ISSUE 34

Fiction by **Shaenon K. Garrity**
Poetry by **Kenzie Allen**
Cover Art by **Maryanna Hoggatt**

DAY ONE

ISSUE 35

Fiction by **Christina Yu**
Poetry by **Maya Catherine Popa**
Cover Art by **Forsyth Harmon**

DAY ONE

ISSUE 36

SAVE

Fiction by **Kevin Skiena**
Poetry by **Chloe Martinez**
Cover Art by **Brooke Weeber**